*Astronomical Photography
at the Telescope*

The Great Nebula in Orion. February 6th, 1957. Exposure, 40 minutes. Film, Kodak Panatomic-X, developed in Promicrol, 1:1 dilution, 18 minutes at 20° C. Taken at the Newtonian focus of 6-inch $f/8$ reflector. The distance across the image of the bright portion on the negative is 5 mm, or rather less than ¼ inch.

ASTRONOMICAL PHOTOGRAPHY AT THE TELESCOPE

THOMAS RACKHAM
F.R.A.S.

With a Foreword by
W. H. STEAVENSON
Gresham Professor in Astronomy

SECOND EDITION

FABER AND FABER
24 Russell Square
London

First published in mcmlix
Second edition mcmlxi
by Faber and Faber Limited
24 Russell Square, London WC1
Printed in Great Britain by
Ebenezer Baylis and Son, Limited
The Trinity Press, Worcester, and London

To

PATRICK MOORE

Contents

7

Illustrations

9

ILLUSTRATIONS

Acknowledgements

Astronomical books sometimes contain celestial photographs that have been taken by astronomers working with the world's largest telescopes. Having admired such pictures, many amateur astronomers must have yearned to do similar work in the hope that their small telescopes could be made to yield good photographs of the heavenly bodies. The aim of this book is to show how the reader may accomplish this without stumbling into numerous pitfalls that lie along his path.

I think it is true to say that nearly every book owes its existence to someone who first suggested to the author that it should be written. At all events this statement is true of this book, and I gratefully acknowledge the enthusiastic help freely given to me by Mr. Patrick Moore, and for the initial stimulus which he provided. Sincere thanks are due to Dr. W. H. Steavenson who read and made valuable suggestions for the improvement of the manuscript, and who generously allowed me to use his 30-inch reflector for astronomical photography. I am also indebted to Mr. F. Webber who turned a kindly but critical eye on my chemistry.

Lastly, I must acknowledge the help of Messrs. Chance-Pilkington Optical Works, Pilkington Brothers Ltd., who allowed me to reproduce the transmission curves of two of their ultra-violet filters.

Preface to the Second Edition

In the first edition of *Astronomical Photography at the Telescope* it seems that I erred mainly by omission; so this time, I have attempted to make amends by including extra information on photographic photometry and the keeping of photographic records. Also, there has been some demand for knowledge of simple astronomical photography that can be effected without expensive apparatus. Well, I have gone further than this, for some of the experiments that I describe near the end of this book require no apparatus at all, so there are no longer any valid excuses for astrophotographic inactivity.

Nevertheless the original intention to provide a useful photographic manual for the owner of the small telescope still remains, and I hope that those readers who derive pleasure from doing the simple experiments will feel the urge to continue their studies of the night skies with telescopes of their own.

Foreword

No serious student of Astronomy can fail to be impressed by the vital part now played by photography in nearly all branches of the science; and it is hardly surprising that to almost every amateur observer there comes, sooner or later, the urge to try the effect of turning his telescope into an astronomical camera.

In most cases the experimenter is content with a few snapshots of the Moon, taken at the focal plane of his telescope. These he pastes with pride into his observing notebook; after which, having thus purged his system of the photographic 'bug', he returns to the visual work for which his instrument is really better suited.

But Mr. Rackham's book is addressed to those who take the matter much more seriously; for he shows how the amateur can, with due attention to detail, produce results that may be of real scientific value.

In fact he has himself demonstrated in the past that photographs taken with quite a small home-made telescope can usefully supplement the visual observations made with the same or other instruments; and that, in the case of the planetary atmospheres, it is possible to record features that are altogether inaccessible to the human eye.

His own success is the greatest encouragement that could be given to his readers to follow his example.

W. H. STEAVENSON
Gresham Professor in Astronomy

Cambridge
January 1959

CHAPTER 1

Aims and Targets

Astronomical photography is not a new subject, and much has been written about it during the last fifty years or so. A good deal of careful searching will be needed to unearth this literature, much of which is confined to the pages of scientific journals and papers.

For the amateur, several useful guides to celestial photography have been published. Perhaps the most famous is the late Professor E. S. King's *Manual of Celestial Photography*[1] which appeared in 1931. A lifetime of experience went into this book and it would be difficult to better Professor King's treatment of the subject.

Broadly speaking, astronomical photography presents two distinct facets. Firstly, there is stellar photography involving large areas of the night sky at a time. This aspect was well covered in the above mentioned book which is one reason why it is only briefly described in the present one.

Secondly, we can use the telescope itself as a camera to obtain enlarged views of our more immediate neighbours in space.

Stellar Photography

Let us consider the intrinsic differences between these two photographic methods. As regards the first, most of the stars are too faint for ordinary 'snapshot' work and long exposures are needed to record them. For the same reason, large apertures are required to collect their light, and these are sometimes beyond the resources of the amateur. Furthermore, the Earth's diurnal motion

[1] King, E. S. *A Manual of Celestial Photography*. Eastern Science Supply Company, Boston, 1931.

17

imparts an apparent east-west movement to these bodies, and this must be skilfully counteracted by the photographer. If he fails to do so, the images will 'trail' across the photographic plate.

At the present time in Great Britain, Schmidt cameras and the like are for the most part only found within the precincts of professional observatories. Amateurs, with few exceptions, must be content with the 'slower' camera of smaller aperture. This he sometimes mounts jockey-wise upon his refracting or reflecting telescope, and, using the larger instrument solely for guiding, commences his exposure upon a selected area of sky.

The night sky can be photographed by almost any camera, providing the lens is reasonably figured and can be guided accurately with a good telescope upon a good mounting. Even a miniature camera can be used to fulfil this purpose: I have used my 35mm. Voigtlander Vito II in this way with encouraging results.

If we wish to photograph whole constellations, large star clusters, distended nebulae, comet tails and meteor trails, we must use the first method, as they can occupy large areas of sky.

Possessors of telescopes will readily appreciate why it would be difficult or impossible to photograph these objects with their instruments: the area of sky covered by the field of the telescope is too small. The prime focal plane of my 6-inch telescope is 49 inches from the mirror and the photographic field is restricted by the draw-tube to less than $1\frac{1}{2}$ square degrees of sky. Visually, the field is more severely limited according to the eyepiece used. With higher power eyepieces it is impossible to view the whole of the lunar disc simultaneously. The angular diameter of the Moon, as all observers know, is about half a degree, and its disc can only be viewed in its entirety with low power eyepieces.

Choice of Subjects—the Sun

Before we go on to discuss the various problems which are encountered in telescopic photography, let us consider some of the objects which will be our targets. First in size, luminosity and importance is the Sun, the only star in the whole Universe whose disc is visible. One of the main photographic problems with the Sun is its abundance of light, which is far in excess of the camera's requirements; its brightness must therefore be reduced before the Sun can be easily or safely photographed. From the amateur's point of view the study of sunspots is probably the most rewarding pursuit, and a series of photographs showing the birth, life and decay of large groups of sunspots makes a valuable record. Whole disc records showing the rotation of the Sun can also be of considerable interest and can be attempted with very small telescopes. A small telescope with a camera attachment will also record the progress of the Moon in front of the Sun during an eclipse. Partial eclipses are far more frequent than total eclipses, which seem to delight in happening in remote and inaccessible places. Unless the Sun is completely covered by the Moon there is no chance of photographing the solar Corona or the 'streamers' curving away from the poles. A patient solar photographer could obtain whole disc views of the Sun at six-month intervals. The image obtained early in January would be larger than the one taken in July with exactly the same apparatus, because the Earth is closer to the Sun in January (though the benefit of this is lost to people living, as we do, far from the equator.) If these two pictures are cut in half and one half of one mounted close to one half of the other, the difference in size will be apparent.

The Moon

Our nearest neighbour in space, the Moon, is without doubt the most rewarding of all the celestial bodies for the visual observer with a small telescope. The same is true of the photographer. In fact, the aspiring celestial photographer would be well advised to concentrate on the Moon. I would go further and say that until the beginner has obtained excellent detailed views of the lunar surface it would be a waste of time and film to attempt planetary work at all. This may seem rather dogmatic, and I do not expect unanimous agreement on this point. Nevertheless the Moon is a wonderful subject to photograph: it presents an enormous wealth of detail, and the contrast between the brilliantly sunlit craters and mountains and their jet-black shadows gives the surface almost another dimension.

Whole disc photographs of the Moon are easily procured, and this type of photography is the nearest approach to 'snapshot' work that we shall encounter. Whole disc records of a full Moon show no shadows at all, but the bright lunar rays, radiating from such craters as Tycho and Copernicus, are then seen at their best. The dark plains, or maria, which looked like seas to the earlier observers with their imperfect telescopes, are also of interest. It is much easier to trace the rays across them than across the rugged and broken terrain which covers the greater part of the Moon's southern hemisphere. The nature of these rays is still not fully understood, and a detailed map of them would be a valuable acquisition. Whole disc records are also useful during lunar eclipses, which occur when the Moon, Earth and Sun are directly in line, the Earth being in between. It is the Earth's shadow, much larger than the Moon, which falls upon the lunar surface and darkens it.

Close-up views of the Moon's surface can provide data for selenographers in their work of mapping the Moon. Many wonderful photographs have been taken by the larger telescopes and the detailed maps we now possess are largely based upon these. Such photographs are not often forthcoming, however, as these telescopes are primarily 'light collectors' designed for the study of distant galaxies—a programme which keeps them always busy. Often a lunar picture showing the surface under a different illumination will help to fill in a blank in our maps. The shape of a shadow in a crater may give clues to the unusual shape of the crater itself. A photograph of a certain formation taken at the same time as a drawing is made of it can also be valuable. Even today there are imperfectly known formations in the Moon's libratory regions. Photography would help here.

The Sun and Moon are about the same angular size—approximately half a degree in diameter. Our task, from the dimensional point of view, may be likened to that of photographing a halfpenny at a distance of about nine feet, for a halfpenny seen from this distance subtends the same angle as the Sun and Moon in the sky. The Sun is so bright that there is no difficulty in enlarging its image to almost any manageable size. The Moon is less co-operative in this respect.

The Planets

What of the planets? The way of the planetary photographer is beset with obstacles, and if he is to prevail, he must be cunning and use his apparatus at maximum efficiency. The first striking difference between the Sun or Moon and the planets is the tremendous disparity of their sizes as seen from the Earth. All observers know that the planet Jupiter is the largest in the Solar System. The volume of the globe of Jupiter is more than a thousand times as great as that of the Earth. Jupiter is never-theless so far from us that we can never see its disc without optical aid.

The angular diameter of Jupiter varies between 30 and 50 seconds of arc, with a mean value of approximately 40 seconds of arc (one degree is equal to 60 minutes of arc, or 3,600 seconds of arc). The Sun and Moon are around 1,800 seconds of arc in diameter, so that Jupiter's mean diameter is about one fiftieth of the Moon's, or about equal to that of a fifty-mile crater on the Moon. This is not a very large angle, but it is as big as any we shall find among the planets, except for Venus, which occasionally exceeds this when it is nearest to the Earth and almost in line with the Sun.

Jupiter never presents a crescent to the Earth, but it does exhibit gibbous phases which can be recorded photographically. The great elliptical disc is crossed by parallel dusky markings whose forms are constantly changing as they rotate at varying speeds in the Jovian atmosphere. We can see only the outer atmospheric envelope of the planet. What lies below is a mystery.

The four Galilean moons of Jupiter can be seen with binoculars and their constantly changing patterns can always be relied upon to provide interesting phenomena for the observer. At times they disappear into the immense shadow of the planet or behind the gigantic bulk of the planet itself. The transits of the satellites across the sunlit face of Jupiter can also be observed; although they may disappear completely when projected on the planet, their progress can often be followed by watching their tiny shadows on the Jovian disc. Much of this activity and the shadow phenomena can be photographed. Mr. H. E. Dall of Luton, a well-known amateur astronomer, in 1956 secured pictures of Jupiter with not one, but three satellite shadows upon it simultaneously!

Saturn, the ringed planet, is neither as bright nor as large (in angular measure) as Jupiter. This is not surprising, since it is nearly twice as far away from the Sun. Saturn's maximum angular diameter is only 20 seconds of arc. The entire ring system subtends approximately the same angle as Jupiter. Saturn is a wonderful object in the telescope. The rings, and possibly the bands which are seen on the planet itself, can be photographed. Unfortunately, for northern observers, Saturn is not likely to be well placed in the sky for some few years to come. The planet revolves about the Sun once in thirty years. It entered the southern celestial hemisphere in the autumn of 1951 and will not return to the northern hemisphere until 1966.

Uranus, Neptune and Pluto are too remote from the Earth for detailed photography, though their positions among the stars can be recorded; the minor planets, or Asteroids, can be found in the same way.

What of the planets whose size and position in the Solar System most nearly resemble the Earth's—Mercury, the nearest to the Sun, Venus, the brightest, and Mars, sometimes described as the Red Planet?

Mercury is too small for amateur photography; its average angular diameter is not much greater than that of Uranus. Above all, it is far too close to the Sun and is never seen in a really dark sky. Venus, on the other hand, is well worth studying with the camera, and its cloud-laden atmosphere can be recorded by certain techniques which will be described in a later chapter. Venus exhibits phases rather like our Moon but, unlike the Moon, appears to change in size considerably. Its angular diameter ranges from 10 seconds of arc to more than 1 minute—a six-fold range in apparent size, which is exceeded only by Mars.

Mars occupies the orbit immediately outside the Earth's, and to an observer on this planet the Earth would pass through a succession of phases similar to that which we observe in the case of Venus or Mercury. Mars is the most earthlike of the planets although it is smaller, being little more than half the diameter of the Earth. It is also the only other body, apart from the Moon, which shows well confirmed surface markings. Bright polar caps, clouds and what are usually described as dust storms are among its observable features. The dark surface markings are sometimes nearly obliterated by these so-called dust storms; this was the case in September 1956, when the planet's opposition should have been particularly favourable, but in fact on some nights almost no surface detail could be seen. Markings, when they are visible, can be captured by the camera when the planet is comparatively near to the Earth. The angular diameter of Mars never exceeds 25 seconds of arc, and its mean opposition diameter is 19 seconds of arc.

So much for the planets. Briefly then, our targets include the Sun, Moon, Venus, Mars, Jupiter and Saturn. Between them they are able to supply the astronomical photographer with plenty of enjoyable labour. If he should consider this list too short, there are other and less parochial objects in the night sky to tax his skill. For example, he might try guiding his telescope and camera on the well-known Orion Nebula. From a host of suitable objects we might mention the Pleiades, the Double Cluster in Perseus, the Great Cluster in Hercules, the Andromeda Nebula, the Ring Nebula in Lyra and many more. When he tires of these he can test his apparatus on binary stars, variable stars and comets. Nor must he lose the chance of photographing a nova when next one flares up. In short, there is enough work to last the average amateur several lifetimes.

The 6-inch reflecting telescope

It should be emphasized here and now that much of this work can be carried out with nothing more elaborate than a 6-inch reflecting telescope. This size is a popular one among amateur astronomers the world over. It is sometimes described as the smallest reflector for serious and worthwhile astronomical observation.

In its Newtonian form, its usefulness lies in its versatility. With additional lenses and eyepieces, solar, lunar and planetary images can be enlarged to suitable dimensions for photography. On the other hand, without these supplementary lenses, the focal images of nebulae and star clusters can be photographed fairly efficiently despite the instrument's large focal ratio (usually about 8). Furthermore it is an excellent visual instrument.

The 6-inch reflector enjoys certain advantages over its bigger brothers. The mirror or speculum quickly reaches thermal equilibrium, so that the instrument can be put quickly into use. The observer does not have to risk his neck on a towering observing ladder. The mounting can be either permanent or portable, though a permanent mounting and observing hut have much to recommend them. There is no doubt that the performance of a good 6-inch telescope, properly mounted, will surpass that of much larger instruments inadequately mounted.

It would be misleading not to mention at least two of the disadvantages of so small a telescope: its poor light grasp and resolving power, both of which are proportional to the square of the diameter of the mirror. Not true! R.P. ∝ Diam., not D²

It may be true that we can never hope to match the quality and resolution of the photographs taken with larger telescopes; but given good atmospheric conditions, first-class optical surfaces, skill, ingenuity and a liberal ration of luck, we may surprise even ourselves.

CHAPTER 2

Photographic Materials and Processes

Any book purporting to deal with some aspect of photography must of necessity, sooner or later, attempt to describe the materials and processes involved. In this book it would seem more convenient to do this sooner rather than later. This will give the newcomer the opportunity to learn some of the bare essentials while providing a useful stimulus to the memories of those readers who may have lost touch with the subject. It must be emphasized that what follows is simply a condensed account of the general outlines of the subject; particular techniques will be dealt with in later chapters.

The photographic plate or film is merely a support for the light-sensitive emulsion; in the same way, this page may be regarded as the support for the words printed upon it. Plates are made of thin glass which, though breakable, is remarkably free from such troubles as warping and thermal expansion and contraction. In addition, glass is chemically inert and is not attacked by any of the normal photographic chemicals. Film, on the other hand, is flexible, and long strips can therefore be coated with photographic emulsion; it can be rolled up and stored in metal containers—making possible the moving film which plays such a large part in modern entertainment. In the early days of the moving picture film was made of celluloid, a dangerous and inflammable material; nowadays, the safer non-inflammable cellulose acetate film is preferred. Like glass, it is transparent, but it can be scratched fairly easily and seems to resent lying flat; it is affected by heat and is attacked by certain solvents. If this sounds pessimistic, let it be hastily added that there is no need to scratch it; it can be persuaded to lie reasonably flat; and in any case why pour solvents over it?

These two materials are not the only ones which can be coated on one side with photographic emulsions. Paper, cloth and other substances can also be used if occasion demands, and, as we shall see, photographic papers are important and essential weapons in the photographic armoury. For purposes of simplicity, when discussing plates and films I shall use the term 'plate' with the tacit assumption that what is said applies equally to film.

The very thin film of emulsion which coats one surface of a photographic plate contains light-sensitive salts suspended in gelatin. There are other ingredients too, depending on the type of plate. The gelatin fulfils several important functions. Firstly, it maintains an even distribution of the microscopic grains of silver salts that are embedded in it. Some of these are on or near the surface, but most of them are in the interior of the gelatin layer. The gelatin must therefore be transparent, or the light will not reach these sub-surface salts and they will undergo no photo-chemical change. The gelatin also allows the chemical solutions to reach the embedded silver salts; were this not so, no development would take place. In addition, a restraining action ensures that only the silver grains that have been exposed to light are changed by development.

Plates as supplied by the manufacturer are carefully wrapped in light-tight boxes. On no account must they be examined in ordinary lighting, for they are photosensitive and will be immediately ruined. Special safelights are available for certain types of plates—but not all. It is best to store them in a cool cupboard, and to handle them only when absolutely necessary. On no account touch the surface of the emulsion: plates must always be held by the edges and if laid down the emulsion should be uppermost, so as to avoid scratches. This surface is all too easily damaged. Plates are generally packed two together with the emulsions facing but not touching. Sometimes, when plates have to be manipulated in total darkness, it is difficult to determine the emulsion side; a useful dodge which usually settles the problem is to insert a small corner of the plate between the lips. The side of the plate tending to cling to the lips is the emulsion side. Never leave the box of plates open, and make sure that they are all returned to their box before switching on the light.

An Experiment

Having acquired a box of plates, let's use one of them. Suppose we lay it on a table with the emulsion uppermost and place a penny on the centre of it. Now, for a brief instant we switch on an electric lamp, several feet above the plate. The penny is removed. What changes have taken place in the photographic emulsion?

In the first place, if we were to examine the plate under a suitable safelight, we should see no outward or visible change whatever. Nevertheless a change has taken place. What is termed a latent image of the penny has been formed in the emulsion by the action of the light. In other words, where light has fallen upon the emulsion, some subtle photochemical change has occurred in the grains of silver salts. The grains sheltered by the penny remain unaffected. This action is extremely complicated and is even today not fully understood by chemists.

The Developing Process

The next operation is to develop our photographic plate. Only by doing this can we change the latent image of the penny into a visible one. Development is carried out by immersing the plate in a solution of various chemicals in carefully graded proportions. There is an embarrassingly large number of developers available for the experimenter to choose from these days. He would be well advised to persevere with one or two until he has a good working knowledge of them. All developers have the same essential function: they reduce to metallic silver the grains of silver salts which have been exposed to light. This means that the exposed grains darken as they change into silver under the action of the developer.

Without going too deeply into this very complicated subject of developing, we may say that all developers are able to extract the halogen from the silver salts in the emulsion. Halogens are a group of chemical substances (most of them rather unpleasant) which include bromine and chlorine. From these are prepared silver bromide and silver chloride, the light-sensitive salts we find in our emulsions. Collectively, they are known as silver halides. The developer is able to remove the halide portion of the salt, thereby reducing the grain to spongy metallic silver. The halogen is absorbed in the developer.

Manufacturers often recommend certain types of developers for use with specified photographic emulsions. This is to help the user to get the full benefit of the desirable characteristics of each; it is no good dipping an emulsion in any developer which happens to be handy and hoping to get satisfactory results. It is advisable to make careful note of any data supplied by the makers of both plates and developers.

Going back to our plate, waiting for us in the developing dish, we see that changes have, in fact, taken place. In the subdued glow of the safelight, the plate no longer has a uniform appearance. The light portion which was shielded by the penny is now surrounded by a black area reaching to the edges of the plate. There are no intermediate tones—just black and white, or what looks as if it might be white if it could be viewed in white light. This transformation did not take place very quickly. For some few seconds after the plate had been immersed in the developing solution no changes were to be seen at all. Then, very gradually, the exposed area round the latent image of the penny began to darken and went through all the shades of grey until it was completely black. The process took several minutes.

The Fixing Process

This is not the end of the processing of the plate; we are, in fact, at this stage only about half-way. So far, we have obtained a white silhouette of the penny against a black background. Now if we were misguided enough to switch on the electric light we used in the first place to make the exposure, we should soon see the light portion of the emulsion begin to darken too; and in a short time this would be as dark as the rest of the plate. To prevent this from happening and to make the white area permanent, the plate must be immersed in a fixing solution. This is ready waiting in a shallow dish close to the developing dish. All solutions are prepared in bright illumination before the developing session begins. (Some developers are light sensitive and, for preference, should be stored in brown glass bottles in a cool and dark cupboard.)

The universal fixing solution is sodium thiosulphate, better known as hypo. Whereas the photographer is sometimes baffled by the very large number of developers available to him, the choice of fixing solutions presents no problem at all.

In order to make the white silhouette of our penny permanent, all the light-sensitive silver halide grains must be removed. This is the function of the hypo. It permeates the gelatin of the emulsion in a similar way to the developer and dissolves the unwanted grains of silver halide. When these have been removed the bright light can be restored without hurting the plate. Fixing does not occur instantaneously and it is safer to wait about three minutes before switching on the light. By this time the silver halide will have gone from the emulsion, leaving mainly metallic silver, which is permanent.

This is the basic idea behind fixing. In practice, however, there are difficulties which are got round by mixing one or two more ingredients into the fixing solution. When the plate is taken from the developing dish it brings a small amount of the developer with it. This is not only on the surface of the emulsion, but also in the gelatin itself. A quick rinse under the tap will remove the surface developer, but the other will remain. In other words, the emulsion carries some of the developer into the fixing solution and, if the developer is still active, it will reduce some of the halide grains which should be dissolving in the hypo. This, in turn, can result in unsightly stains, which will ruin the fixed plate. To keep these troubles at bay, it is usual to mix a small amount of acid with the

29

fixer. Hence acid-hypo. The acid neutralizes or 'kills' the alkali of the developer, which then ceases to work.

Another way of dealing with this trouble is to use an intermediate stop-bath before fixing. A stop-bath does what its name implies—it stops the developer working. It usually consists of a dilute acid such as acetic acid.

Other chemicals used in fixing solutions are hardeners. Again the name betrays their function, which is to harden or toughen the gelatin of the emulsion so that it is less liable to damage from heat and abrasion. There are other ingredients, but these are the main ones used by amateurs.

Having fixed our plate, we are still not finished. The fixing solution, if given time, will attack and bleach the emulsion. Furthermore, the plate will not keep indefinitely if any of the hypo remains in it. Therefore the plate must be washed thoroughly, either in several changes of water, or better still, under a running tap. After this, it must be placed in a drying rack in a warm, but not hot, place. When the plate is dry, processing is complete.

The Negative

When dried our plate can be examined under normal lighting. If we look through the central circular patch we shall find that it is transparent enough for objects to be identified through it, whereas the dark region outside it is almost opaque. Something seems wrong about this, for instead of having an image of a dark penny on a light background, we now have a light image on a dark background.

This is clearly the opposite of what we require and is called a photographic negative. All negatives show the blacks as whites, the dark greys as off-whites, the light greys as dark greys and the whites as blacks. In other words the tones of the original subject are reversed on the negative. To obtain a more faithful rendering of our dark penny against a light background we must make a positive of it. In most cases this would be done upon photographic paper but, since we have not yet discussed this aspect of photography, we had better use another of our plates.

The Positive

To make a positive transparency on a plate, which is exactly what a lantern slide is, we lay the plate down as before with the emulsion side uppermost. The negative is placed on this, with its emulsion side down—*i.e.*, the two emulsions should be in contact. This ensures two things: first, that the sharpness of the negative image is retained in the positive and secondly, that the positive does not turn out to be a mirror-image of the original. In our case with the penny, it would not matter very much, but in the case of a star photograph it would render the constellations unrecognizable.

When the negative has been placed on the new plate, an exposure can be made exactly as before. As we are dealing only with blacks and whites, the length of the exposure will be about the same. The negative is removed to a safe place and plate No. 2 is submitted to exactly similar processing as No. 1. The earlier stages are, of course, performed in the glow of the safelight. If all goes well, we should finish up with an opaque circular patch—the image of our penny—against an almost clear plate. This could be projected on to a screen and we could compare this with another piece of clear glass with a penny stuck to the middle of it.

These then are the basic ideas of the negative and positive. In most cases the negative is made as a transparency on glass or film. The positive is nearly always a print on photographic paper unless we want to project it on to a screen.

Before proceeding, there are one or two points which ought to be emphasized. In the first place, it might seem a long and laborious task to make a negative of a certain subject and then a positive before we can assess what we have recorded. This is to some extent true, but when the operator has gained some experience he will be able to anticipate the finished positive by examining the negative—particularly so with lunar and planetary photographs. (Negatives of human faces do admittedly look grotesque,

31

and apart from seeing that focusing is sharp, it is difficult to judge if the finished product will be flattering or otherwise to the sitter.) There is one important advantage connected with the negative—we can print from it as many positives as we want.

The Emulsion

The light-sensitive photographic emulsion has often been compared with the light-sensitive layer in the human eye—the retina. Each can differentiate between degrees of light and shade, but the eye has the additional ability to record movement in the ever-changing patterns presented to it, whereas the photographic emulsion can select one event only from a continuous sequence. If we wish to record the sequence, we can do so with moving film consisting of thousands of separate frames or pictures. When these are shown in quick succession, the eye can be deluded into accepting this as real movement. In this respect the eye is far superior to film.

The photographic emulsion does, however, enjoy one very important advantage over the eye: the effect of light on it is cumulative. We cannot see anything more clearly by gazing fixedly at it for a long time, but this can be done by a photographic plate. If dim light is allowed to fall on it for a short time nothing will be recorded upon the developed plate. On the other hand, a long exposure with the same dim light will gradually produce photochemical changes in the exposed portions of the emulsion, resulting in some blackening of the reduced silver halide grains upon development. This is the reason for the long exposures employed by astronomers when hunting for very faint objects. Star images must be kept accurately aligned on the plate so that each one is given the maximum opportunity to concentrate upon its own little group of emulsion grains. Wandering star images affect the emulsion like unfocused star images: their light is shared by a large number of silver halide grains, and, if the star is faint, it is quite possible that none of the grains will be activated.

A first magnitude star is one hundred times as bright as one of the sixth magnitude. When we photograph the sky there is no way of adjusting the amount of light from the stars, so, if we correctly expose for sixth magnitude stars, the brighter ones must be grossly over-exposed. This means that the bright stars do not appear as tiny points but as enlarged circular discs. Obviously, an excess of metallic silver has been formed. Several agencies have been invoked to produce this. Firstly, when bright light falls on an emulsion there is bound to be some scatter of the light and if this is bright enough, or persists long enough, it will affect the silver halide grains around the point where the light itself is concentrated. This is not just a surface phenomenon but goes right down into the gelatin. A very bright light may even be reflected into the gelatin again from the rear surface of the plate, causing more trouble. This latter nuisance is partly countered by 'backing' the plate with a pigment whose colour depends largely on the type and purpose for which the plate is used. Halation is the name given to this effect, since haloes often form round the brighter star images on unbacked plates.

To some extent light scatter or diffusion in a photographic emulsion is always present, which means we can never faithfully record the tiny star images which, given perfect lenses and mirrors, and perfect 'seeing', would fall on our emulsion. These images consist, for the most part, of a tiny disc (the Airy disc), into which about 80% of the light forming the image is concentrated. The fact that a point source is recorded by the emulsion as a disc, sets a definite limit to the resolving power.

The visual resolving power of a telescope can be gauged by its ability to separate two star images. Theory and practice (involving Airy's diffraction images and Dawes' experimental work with a 1-inch aperture) closely agree. In both cases, it can be shown that for a given wavelength the resolution of a telescope depends upon aperture only. Large mirrors are able to split close double stars that are far beyond the limits of smaller telescopes, because the larger the aperture, the smaller the diffraction disc of a star. Using bright stars, the amateur can soon see for himself the results of 'stopping down' his telescope.

33

Inevitably it is necessary to employ high magnifications for the visual separation of close double stars. The same is true of photographic work, for diffusion in the emulsion severely limits the resolving power. The effect can be minimized in two ways. The first is to keep the images small, by under-exposing. In this way, fewer of the silver halide grains outside the perimeters of the star images are subjected to photochemical change. Secondly, we can increase the effective focal length of the telescope and the images will have greater separation. (At the same time, the brightness of the image will be diminished, not in proportion to focal length, but as the square of it. Thus, if the focal length is doubled, the exposure must be four times as long.[1])

Graininess

We have seen how an emulsion consists of grains of silver halide suspended uniformly in a thin layer of gelatin. Singly, these grains are much too small to constitute any menace to the photographer. Collectively, they can and do. The process of development enlarges them, and even the shapes of the original grains change as they are reduced to metallic silver. Over-development enlarges them still more. But even this would not interfere with the work of the average photographer because of the extremely small size of these grains—of the order of one thousandth of a millimetre in diameter. There is another and more troublesome phenomenon which sometimes causes serious trouble. During development there seem to be local migrations of the silver grains, which actually move through the gelatin with a tendency to clump together in small groups. The distances involved are microscopic, and the effect is invisible to the naked eye. It is only when the negative has to be enlarged by projection, for the production of enlarged positives, that the grainy appearance reveals its objectionable presence. It does, in fact, set an upper limit to the degree of enlargement

[1] This is approximately so. In practice, seeing and guiding errors enlarge the star images, causing a dilution of the light, and this leads to longer exposures.

obtainable from a negative. It is important to differentiate between the two sorts of grain. The 'graininess' caused by the clumping together of minute silver grains during development is the bane of all photographers using 'fast' miniature emulsions.

It is an unfortunate fact that the extremely fast emulsions invariably suffer from this defect, while the slow ones enjoy almost complete immunity. Between these two extremes are the medium-speed emulsions which are troubled less by graininess; they possess some of the attractive qualities of both fast and slow emulsions.

The resolving power of an emulsion is a measure of its ability to define patterns consisting of a large number of black and white lines; it is then said to be able to resolve a certain number of lines per millimetre. This is not wholly dependent upon the grain structure of the emulsion, for both contrast and processing play an important part. More will be said about this later.

Emulsion Speed

Meanwhile, let us clarify our ideas concerning the nature of photographic 'speed'. Speed is the rate at which something is done—*i.e.*, one of the factors involved is time.

The same is true in photography. Given a constant source of illumination, the speed of a photographic emulsion, in the widest sense, is the rate at which metallic silver is formed per unit of time. We must not forget the processes by which metallic silver is formed: first, the exposure to light, involving time; then the developing and fixing, etc. For the purposes of the discussion we can ignore the processing, and assume that when light falls upon an emulsion the silver automatically forms. Under these conditions and with our constant source of illumination, fast emulsions will show signs of blackening before slower ones.

If we take two photographic plates, one rated as fast and the other slow, we can conduct some interesting experiments. Their grain-size will be proportional to their speed—this is true of all photographic emulsions. Both will be processed for the same length of time in the same developer. They will be laid, emulsions up, side by side on a table and submitted to the same low intensity illumination.

With the use of masks, strips of both emulsions are given identical simultaneous exposures. A large number of these are made and each is carefully timed to be twice as long as its predecessor. Starting with one second, the next will be two and will be followed by four seconds, passing on to eight, sixteen, thirty-two etc., until all available space has been used on both plates. There is a good reason for timing the exposures in this way.

When processing has been completed we can observe and analyse the results of our experiment. Casual inspection will reveal certain similarities. Both plates, for example, are free of metallic silver at one end and are black at the other, with strips of different shading in between.

More detailed observation of the faster plate shows no blackening in the first strip. Slight darkening occurs in the second and, from then on, there is a series of ever darkening strips. The last three strips, at the opposite end of the plate, are uniformly dark—but not jet black. There are no real blacks to be seen at all upon the faster plate.

The slower plate exhibits marked differences from the first. Instead of just one blank strip at the beginning, there are several before darkening commences. As this proceeds, each adjacent strip shows a much greater degree of darkening. Indeed, over about one quarter of this plate the darkening is comparable with that of the final strips of the faster plate. Neither does it stop there, but continues to darken still more until it becomes truly black. The last three strips are uniformly black—jet black.

The time-honoured method used for comparing two such emulsions, is to measure the darkening of all the segments of each and to plot the results on a graph. This is easier to write than to do, for, if the main criterion is accuracy, delicate and expensive optical instruments have to be used for the measuring. Very briefly, the amount of incident light falling upon one side of the emulsion is compared with the transmitted light emerging from the other side. Thus, if the emulsion is completely black, there will be no transmitted light. If it is clear, then nearly all the incident light emerges as transmitted light. The transmission of an emulsion or filter is an important factor and is derived by dividing the intensity of the transmitted light, It, by that of the incident light, I. Thus:

Transmission $= It/I$

The transmission factor approaches 1 for clear glass and 0 for dense black; in the latter case no light is transmitted, and the numerator is zero.

The reciprocal of transmission is opacity. Thus:

Opacity $= I/It$.

It will be apparent from this, since It for black areas can be extremely small, that opacity can attain very large numerical values; also that when most of the light is transmitted, the opacity will approach 1 without ever quite reaching it. For the transmission of all the incident light can never be realized in practice.

Let us assume we have measured all the various degrees of darkening of our two emulsions, and that 10,000 is the greatest value obtained for opacity. Or, to put it another way, that the transmitted light intensity was only 1/10,000 that of the incident light.

Now we can get on with the graph. The left-hand axis will be graduated in degrees of darkening—*i.e.*, opacity. The way to do this is to regard the lower end of it, where it joins the horizontal axis, as representing no darkening at all; as we travel up the axis the amount of darkening increases to our maximum opacity value of 10,000. Starting with 1 at the origin of the axis, the next major division will be 10, followed at equal intervals by 100, 1,000 and 10,000.

Transmission values could have been inserted too, but not without crowding our graph. Starting at the bottom left, the first number would have been 1 followed at equal intervals by ·1, ·01, ·001 and ·0001—the transmission values corresponding respectively to opacities of 1, 10, 100, 1,000 and 10,000.

Along the horizontal axis, at equal intervals, we insert the numbers 1 (at the junction of the axes), then 2, 4, 8, 16, 32 etc.;

these represent the durations of our exposures in seconds. They also represent increasing light intensity, for by keeping exposure times equal but doubling the light intensity for each, almost identical results would have been achieved. Needless to say, in practice the former method is much easier to work than the latter. Our horizontal axis therefore represents light intensity or exposure time; it is impossible to divorce one from the other.

It will be noticed that both our vertical and horizontal axes have been graduated in a non-linear manner. On the opacity scale, identical divisions represent 10 units at the bottom and 9,000 at the top. Likewise, divisions of equal length on the time scale assume larger values the further they are to the right. These are logarithmic scales. Opacity has been purposely plotted on a logarithmic scale to base 10 to give us another factor—density, which is the logarithm to base 10 of opacity. Thus, if we insert beside our vertical scale the numbers, 1, 2, 3 and 4 (the logarithms of 10, 100, 1,000 and 10,000) we shall have evaluated density, whose units are less cumbersome than those of opacity and transmission.

The horizontal axis of our graph is logarithmic, not to base 10, but to base 2. This can be converted to a log base 10 scale without altering anything but the numbers. Where 10 appears we write 1, and where the 100 mark is we put 2, and so on. Having made this slight alteration, we can give the horizontal axis a caption: log to base 10 Exposure. Since exposure is the product of light intensity and time, it follows that log exposure equals log intensity plus log time. Light intensity is measured in foot-candles or metre-candles, and time in seconds.

Our graphical framework is now ready to receive the data derived from measuring the densities of the strips of emulsions. (*see* Figure 1.)

Emulsion Characteristic Curves

We have now obtained what are known as characteristic curves or H and D curves after Hurter and Driffield, who first used this method of plotting emulsion characteristics. By studying such curves we can derive much useful information.

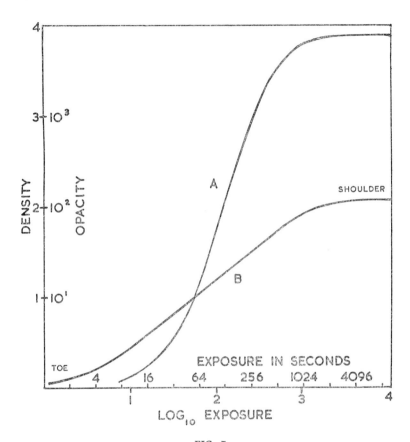

FIG. I

Emulsion characteristic curves

A *is the steep curve of the slower emulsion with its greater density range but reduced exposure latitude. The gently rising curve of the faster emulsion,* B, *indicates more exposure latitude and a smaller density range.* A *is more 'contrasty' than* B.

Starting with similarities, both curves start from 'toes' at their lowest left ends and finish with 'shoulders' at their upper right ends. Between these extremes are substantially straight sections—the working portions of the curves. The following facts are also to be noted:

(1) The curve of the faster emulsion begins further to the left than that of the slower emulsion.

(2) The curve of the faster emulsion rises less steeply.

(3) The shoulder of the faster emulsion curve is lower than that of the slower one.

(4) The straight portion of the faster emulsion curve, by virtue of its gentle slope, covers a greater length of the log exposure axis.

It is easy to see from the two curves, that the one starting nearer the left is the faster (point (1) above). The emulsion has commenced to blacken despite the shorter exposure time. It has less 'inertia' than the slower one.

(2) is bound up with (3), and they can be discussed together. When a curve rises gently, it means photographic darkening is occurring more slowly. The gentle curve belongs to the faster emulsion, and from (1) we can see that although darkening proceeds more slowly, it started earlier. (3) notes the moderate height of the shoulder of the faster curve. On the vertical scale, this corresponds to a restricted range of densities compared with the slower emulsion. This is inextricably bound up with the concept of contrast, but should not be confused with it. Contrast refers to the range of densities likely to be encountered over a restricted length of characteristic curve. Perhaps this is more easily understood if we select a small portion of our log exposure axis and project it vertically to meet the linear portions of both curves. It will then be very apparent that, within the limitations we have set, the range of densities of the slower emulsion is much greater than that of the faster one. Contrast is measured by the slope of the characteristic curve—not the height. Numerical values for contrast are obtained by measuring the angle between the straight part of the curve and a horizontal line, parallel to the log exposure axis; the tangent of this angle gives the required value, and the Greek letter gamma (γ) is often substituted for the word contrast.

An angle of 45° yields a γ value of 1. Such emulsions will record densities without under- or over-emphasis.

The large γ-values of steeply sloping characteristic curves indicate emulsions capable of high contrast—a desirable quality for planetary work. It is most unfortunate that these are always slow emulsions.

(4), the relative length of the log exposure axis covered by the linear portion of the faster curve, can be interpreted in this way. Again, reference to our log exposure axis shows we could select a very wide range of exposure times and still hit the straight working section of the faster curve. When it comes to calculating exposures, we are allowed considerable 'latitude' for errors. Not so with the slower emulsions. With these there is not much 'latitude' because their curves rise too steeply to cover long expanses of the log exposure axis. On the other hand, these curves cover greater extents of the density axis.

We must always try to calculate exposures so we can use the linear portions of the characteristic curves. The 'toe' indicates the region of under-exposure where blackening occurs non-linearly. The 'shoulder' must similarly be avoided, since it represents the region of over-exposure.

There are many factors which influence the slopes of characteristic curves. Different types of developers, temperature variations in developers, under- and over-development, agitation, spectral distribution of illumination—these are only some of them. This is why photography has never been what might be termed an exact science. Even without these variable factors, manufacturers would still be faced with the problem of producing identical emulsions. As things are it is surprising such high standards are maintained.

Returning to the characteristic (or γ) curve, it must be noted that the angle, formed by the linear portion of the curve and the line parallel to the log exposure axis, increases during the developing process. In the early stages of development there is no angle at all, but it commences to grow as density values increase with the formation of metallic silver grains. A maximum angle is reached upon full development when γ is said to be at infinity. At the same time we must not confuse this with the actual value of γ—the tangent of the angle—for, with faster negative emulsions, this is often less than unity. γ infinity is a qualitative term which can be used without having to assign a definite maximum value to γ.

In practice, we never develop negatives to these limits, and ·6 to ·8 of the maximum value of γ should not be exceeded. Maximum γ, or γ infinity, is only produced quickly by using energetic, fast working and contrasty developers. These are invariably grainy developers too—they tend to cause the clumping of grains we seek so desperately to avoid. The low energy, soft-working developers take longer to yield lower values of γ with less graininess.

If development is continued after the maximum slope of the γ curve has been reached, chemical fog will start to develop over the lighter areas of the emulsion; this is the forerunner of the blackening which will eventually extend over the whole plate if the process is allowed to continue. In this case, even the halide grains which have not been subjected to light will darken, and the curve will simply tend to move to the left of the graph without steepening.

For astronomical work it would be fatal to work our emulsions to γ infinity or to use contrasty developers on our precious negatives. Fine-grain developers (of which more later) must always be used.

In passing, it can be said that no universally accepted method of defining emulsion speed exists. It depends largely upon the way the sensitivity of the material is measured, and this in turn varies from place to place and from manufacturer to manufacturer. In the main, the systems are either logarithmic or arithmetical; there are at least eighteen of them.

Colour Sensitivity

Before we leave negative emulsions we must discuss one very important characteristic which, so far, has not been mentioned:

their colour sensitivity. The photographic emulsion, unlike the human eye, is able to see more clearly in the blue and ultra-violet region of the spectrum. This is where 'ordinary' photographic materials perform well; such emulsions are also known as blue-sensitive, and are useful ones for astronomical work. Others can be sensitized for the green as well as for the blue-violet region and are known as ortho- or iso-chromatic; this optimistically implies a similar spectral sensitivity to that of the eye. Further sensitizing for the red will yield panchromatic materials responding to all the visible spectrum, and the ultra-violet as well. They are relatively less sensitive to green, and are insensitive to infra-red radiation. Infra-red sensitive plates and films are also manufactured, and must be stored in cool places—these too have their astronomical uses.

Data sheets supplied by manufacturers sometimes include 'wedge spectrograms' of emulsions showing the reaction to various parts of the spectrum; the higher the curves rise, the greater the sensitivity, and vice versa. A true picture is not always given since it is generally assumed that most photographers use glass lenses which absorb the ultra-violet. Actually, the sensitivity is better in this region than anywhere else.

The wedge spectrogram is a graph in which sensitivity (on the vertical axis) is plotted against wavelength (horizontal axis). They are given for both daylight and tungsten light, since the spectral distributions of the two are so dissimilar—the latter being much richer in red.

Reciprocity Failure

Another phenomenon affecting photographic emulsions is a slowing down of their reaction to light, known as reciprocity failure. It was assumed, many years ago, that the amount of darkening that occured in an emulsion was proportioned to the product of illumination and exposure time. That is, if the exposure were long and the illumination small, the same amount of silver would be formed as in an identical emulsion submitted to proportionately shorter exposures and brighter illuminations. It was left to Schwarzschild, an eminent astronomer of the nineteenth century, to show this was only approximately so. With long exposures, the reaction of the photographic emulsion gradually slows down, and the amount of blackening is not as great in the second hour as it was in the first. Strangely enough, the faster emulsions seem to fatigue more rapidly than slower ones. Using a fast emulsion for a long exposure is rather like asking a hundred yard sprinter to run the mile—he would not be able to maintain his terrific pace for long, and would eventually be passed by his slower competitors.

Photographic Papers

So far photographic papers have only been mentioned in passing. These are the emulsion-coated papers which are used, with certain exceptions, for the production of positive prints and enlargements. The printing process involves chloride and chlorobromide papers which are comparatively insensitive to light, so that operations can be carried on safely under good illumination.

Bromide papers are typical of the ones used for enlarging work. The name reveals the particular silver halide involved, and since our negative materials are known to include the same salt, we should not be too surprised to discover that both types of emulsion have something in common. Spectrally, the bromide material behaves like the blue-sensitive negative emulsion, so we are able to use it in bright safelight illumination of the orange and red region of the spectrum.

Speeds of photographic papers are of little importance, though a word or two should be said about the grades ranging from Extra Soft to Ultra Hard. The soft papers have characteristic curves not unlike those of the faster negative materials; that is, they rise gently and therefore offer a wide range of tones. They are a little faster than hard papers and therefore require shorter exposures. The hard papers, with their steep curves, are characterized by lack of gradation, and tend to confuse whites and light

44

greys and, at the upper end of the curve, blacks and dark greys. With the wrong type of negative these papers will yield objectionable 'soot and whitewash' effects. They do, however, help to restore the balance in weak and 'thin' negatives.

This is as far as we need to go at present into the realms of pure photography. The subject is a vast one, and the purpose of this chapter has been simply to introduce certain important points which will be relevant to what is to follow.

CHAPTER 3

The Astronomical Telescope

Astronomical telescopes fall into two groups—reflectors and refractors. The latter range in size from very small apertures of about 1 inch up to, for amateurs, around 6 inches. Above that, the price of the objective puts refractors beyond the reach of the average pocket. A 6-inch refractor is a large and expensive piece of equipment, and unless the amateur is a sufficiently expert optician to make his own lenses, he will probably content himself with what is sometimes described as the 'poor man's telescope'— the reflector. The reflector carries on where the amateur refractor leaves off. Apertures of from 6 inches to a foot or two are found in amateur hands, while the professional astronomers' instruments culminate in the world-famous 200-inch on Mt. Palomar. The largest telescope owned by an amateur in Great Britain, probably in the world, belongs to Dr. W. H. Steavenson of Cambridge. His mirror has an aperture of 30 inches and weighs approximately 2 cwt. I was privileged to use this telescope for photography on several occasions in 1956, and I can affirm that the equipment to be described later will perform well on the largest as well as on the smallest reflectors. The aim of this book, however, is to show what can be done with the smallest reflectors, of about 6 inches aperture.

First of all, let us discuss the main differences between the two types of telescope in order to discover which is the more suitable for photography.

The Refractor

In a refractor the objective, a lens, is held in a retaining cell at one end of a cylindrical tube, and the eyepiece is arranged in an

46

adjustable draw-tube at the other. The function of the two-lens objective is to supply good quality images for subsequent enlargement by the eyepiece. For visual work the achromatic objective is designed to give optimum results in the green-yellow part of the spectrum to which the eye is most sensitive. Here the images obtained with a good glass are excellent. The secondary spectrum (uncorrected colour) consists of a little residual red and blue which together form a purple fringe around the image.

Here, then, is one objection to the object glass from the photographic point of view. We may focus sharply by eye, only to find the developed image marred by unfocused and more actinic blue-violet images.

A second objection is the loss of light in the objective. With a large lens this can be formidable, since the components are thick and are nearly always separated. With modern coating techniques the 4% loss of light by reflection at each air-to-glass surface can be reduced—but we can do little about the transmission losses in the glass itself. All types of glasses, but especially the denser ones, absorb strongly in the ultra-violet.

Focal Ratios

Before going on to a third objection involving focal ratios, it would perhaps be as well to define this term. The focal ratio of a telescope or camera is the ratio of the focal length of the lens or mirror to its diameter. In other words, the focal length divided by the clear aperture (both measured in the same unit) is the focal ratio, or f/ratio. A 6-inch telescope of 48 inches focal length is said to be working at $f/8$. To the photographer the f/ratio indicates the speed of the lens, and dictates the type of film and duration of exposure required for a given object. Ignoring secondary light losses, all lenses or mirrors of the same focal ratio will need identical exposures and emulsions to give equally bright images of the same object.

Most astronomical refractors have focal ratios of 15 ($f/15$) or thereabouts. And while some of our work has to be done with

47

numerically higher focal ratios than this, there are occasions when we would prefer to employ smaller ones. Photographs of faint and extended objects, such as nebulae and comets, will need nearly four times the exposure with an $f/15$ telescope as with an $f/8$.

This does not mean that owners of refracting telescopes cannot indulge in celestial photography, though the refractor does suffer from certain drawbacks, compared with the reflector.

The Reflector

Here a mirror (or speculum) takes the role of the object glass; it is mounted in a cell at the bottom of the telescope and light therefore has to travel the length of the tube before being reflected back to a smaller mirror near the mouth of the tube, and thence to the eyepiece. The type of reflector most widely used by amateurs, the world over, is undoubtedly the Newtonian, followed in popularity by the Cassegrain. The latter is well suited for planetary photography by virtue of its great focal length.

Let us compare the Newtonian's performance with that of the refractor. We have already said that the finely figured parabolic mirror is squared on to the lower end of the telescope tube. The parallel rays of starlight, having passed down the length of the tube, are reflected from the aluminized or silvered surface of the mirror and would, if permitted, come to focus near the upper end of the tube. A few inches below the focus, however, is fixed a smaller, plane mirror, inclined at an angle of 45°. This is just large enough to collect the light reflected from the primary mirror, so as to occlude the minimum of light entering the telescope.

This diagonal, or flat, deflects the converging cone of light through 90° into the draw-tube containing the eyepiece, which, at the upper end of the telescope, is in a convenient position for the observer.

The overwhelming advantage of the reflector over the refractor is its complete achromatism. Ignoring the eyepiece, the light entering the telescope has nowhere to pass *through* glass, and therefore suffers no dispersion into its spectral colours. The

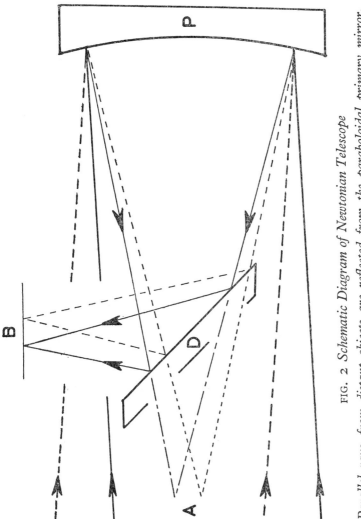

FIG. 2 *Schematic Diagram of Newtonian Telescope*

Parallel rays from distant objects are reflected from the paraboloidal primary mirror, P, and would come to a prime focus at A were they not first deflected by the diagonal, D, to an accessible position at B (the Newtonian focus). Here the images can fall directly upon a photographic emulsion, or be enlarged with additional lenses for both visual and photographic work.

advantage to the astronomical photographer lies in the fact that he can focus by eye in the green-yellow part of the spectrum, confident that he is correctly focusing in all other wavelengths as well—particularly the blue-violet region to which the photographic emulsion is most sensitive.

We have already referred briefly to the large focal ratios of refractors. That of a reflector is seldom greater than $f/10$, and $f/5$ to $f/8$ is more common among amateur instruments. There is no need to reiterate what has already been said concerning the greater photographic 'speed' of smaller focal ratios. On the other hand refractors have one advantage over reflectors: their focal planes are flatter, and the relative freedom from coma resulting from larger focal ratios gives them improved definition at the edge of the field. I have never detected any traces of coma with my 6-inch $f/8$ reflector on 35mm. film, but below about $f/4$ it becomes serious.

Silvering and Aluminizing

For the visual observer a good, freshly deposited film of silver has much to recommend it, for its reflectivity is more than 90% from 4000A (the blue-violet region) throughout the whole visible spectrum and far into the infra-red. Unhappily it does not maintain this performance for very long since it is soon tarnished by harmful chemicals in the atmosphere—chiefly sulphur from chimney smoke—and after a few months the silver film must be renewed. In passing, it is interesting to note that even when the mirror is completely tarnished it still reflects infra-red radiation. The reflectivity of silver drops rapidly in the ultra-violet as far as about 3000A; where, instead of being a reflector, it is a highly efficient transmitter of the ultra-violet. Interesting work on the Moon and the planets has been done by R. W. Wood, using silver films as ultra-violet filters. So if we wish to indulge in ultra-violet photography we must not use silver-coated mirrors.

Aluminium does not enjoy the remarkable properties of freshly deposited silver in the visible region, but it possesses advantages which more than compensate for this. Within a few hours of being deposited upon a mirror it develops a protective, transparent layer of oxide which preserves it for a long time—many years in some recorded cases. (It is this same formation of a film of oxide that makes the soldering of two pieces of aluminium by ordinary methods such a difficult process, for the oxide begins to form immediately the surfaces are cleaned.)

The valuable property of aluminium is its ability to reflect strongly in the ultra-violet region of the spectrum to which 'ordinary' or blue-sensitive photographic materials are most sensitive. In the visible region it maintains high reflectivity and, although not as good as freshly deposited silver, it is superior to slightly tarnished silver. Furthermore, unlike silver, the newly deposited film needs no burnishing.

The performance of a refractor's object glass is somewhat similar to that of a silvered mirror, for neither is efficient in the 3000A to 4000A ultra-violet region. Below 3500A both rapidly fail and become almost totally 'blind' at 3000A.

Summing up the advantages of a reflecting telescope, these are:
(1) Complete achromatism.
(2) Small focal ratio giving more photographic 'speed'.
(3) Ultra-violet sensitivity.
(4) Larger aperture for same financial outlay.

Other advantages involve tube lengths, mountings, etc. The fourth point is important: a 6-inch mirror and diagonal may be bought for about the price of a 3-inch objective, or about one quarter the cost of a complete 3-inch refractor. It need not cost even this if the observer is prepared to grind and polish his own mirror. Patience and time are the main requirements for this task, skill and 'know-how' are the by-products, and many an amateur has persevered to triumph over the recalcitrant glass.

The writer's first primer on mirror making was the late W. F. A. Ellison's *The Amateur's Telescope*[1] which kindled flames of enthusiasm on both sides of the Atlantic. Since then, many books

[1] Ellison, W. F. A. *The Amateur's Telescope,* also contained in *Amateur Telescope Making*, Book I.

have been compiled on the theory and practice of mirror making.

The making of telescope mirrors is, in itself, a satisfying pursuit. There is an undeniable fascination in the quest for absolute perfection of the optical surfaces, even though this must remain an ideal rather than a reality, and many an imperfect mirror has given countless hours of delight to its owner.

Resolving Power

The important quality of any mirror is the final figure given to its surface, and it is this which determines whether it is excellent, or just another piece of polished glass. In the case of the reflecting telescope, the paraboloidal surface has the property of reflecting all rays parallel to its axis to one tiny point in the focal plane. Under perfect conditions, this image will consist of a tiny central disc surrounded by one or two delicate diffraction rings. A mirror capable of doing this is correctly figured and is said to be able to define a star image. Again, under perfect conditions, a high-power eyepiece should not show much enlargement of the star disc, although the diffraction rings will appear larger. Failure to obtain such images points to a faulty mirror or some defect in its support.

An extended object—the Moon for example—can be regarded as a large number of point sources packed so closely as to constitute a continuous surface. The task of the telescope is to render each as a separate entity, so that the image will comprise a large number of tiny but finite diffraction discs. In practice, these and the diffraction rings around them will overlap to a greater or lesser degree according to their various light intensities, and the finest detail will be confused or lost, owing to the overlapping of the discs.

A rule for determining the visual resolution of a telescope was derived empirically by Dawes many years ago. There is no need to go into the theory of this, which is adequately dealt with elsewhere.[1] Briefly it states that 4·56 seconds of arc divided by the aperture of the telescope in inches gives the minimum angular separation that the telescope can achieve for two stars of the same

[1] Sidgwick, J. B. *Amateur Astronomer's Handbook*. Faber, 1954.

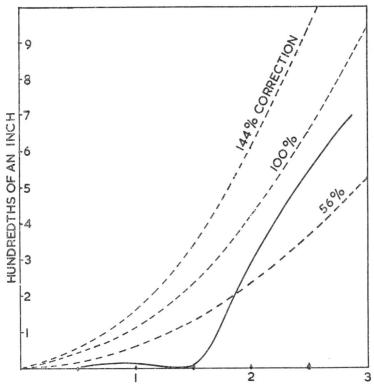

DISTANCE FROM CENTRE OF MIRROR IN INCHES

FIG. 3

We can judge a telescope mirror only by the way it reflects light from its surface.[1] The 100% dotted curve indicates the perfect performance, but for a 6-inch f/8 mirror we are allowed 44% tolerances either side, as shown. Superimposing the unbroken curve, representing the performance of the author's mirror, on that of the 100%, shows that, apart from a small area in the centre, the mirror is excellent.

magnitude. In perfect conditions, a 6-inch telescope should just be able to separate two equally bright stars if they are 0·75 seconds

---

[1] Figure 3 shows how the mirror surface reflects incident light. This is obviously related to, but must not be confused with, the actual shape of the glass surface. F. B. Wright (*Amateur Telescopic Making*, Book I, Chap. 6) deals fully with the problem.

of arc apart. In the focal plane, assuming it to be an $f/8$ telescope, the centres of these images would be separated by about one quarter of one thousandth of an inch, or about six average-sized silver halide grains. No emulsion could resolve two star images as close as this, since the images themselves would be of the order of one thousandth of an inch in diameter.

Dawes' yard-stick cannot be strictly applied to the moon and planets, nor even (without modification) to stars of unequal magnitude. But as long as we use it as Dawes intended, we can predict the performance of a mirror and then attempt to confirm the prediction experimentally. If there is a large measure of agreement the mirror is a good one and will yield good images of extended objects too. A mirror which performs well visually cannot fail to supply good photographic images, and it is nearly always the atmospheric condititions that set the upper limit to photographic resolution.

To perform well, a mirror must be well-nigh perfect—that is, within a few millionths of an inch of the ideal surface. It sometimes takes the amateur mirror maker a long time to get the surface right but it is well worth the additional time and trouble to do so. There are tolerances for every mirror which give the mirror maker a little latitude in the figure. The curve of a paraboloidal mirror flattens towards the edge, which means the outer area of the mirror has a slightly longer focal length than the centre. The difference between a spherical and paraboloidal mirror of a focal ratio of 8 is very slight, and it is customary to work such a mirror to a sphere in the first place, and then to deepen the central regions until the desired curve is achieved. In the case of a 6-inch $f/8$ mirror we are allowed a 44% tolerance on each side of the perfect curve. If the mirror comes within this, its performance will be indistinguishable from the true paraboloidal mirror and, as long as the curve is reasonably regular, it can be considered a fine optical surface. The mirror maker uses a simple but extremely accurate test which can measure the surface to millionths of an inch. The famous Foucault knife-edge test is so sensitive that it will show the bump raised by thermal expansion due to the momentary touch of a finger on the glass surface.

If we plot the differences in the radii of curvature of concentric zones against their respective distances from the centre of the mirror, and insert the perfect performance curve with the 44% tolerance either side of it, we can assess the quality of our 6-inch mirror. This has been done for the author's mirror in Figure 3, but it is important to note that it is the shape of the plotted curve and not its position on the graph that indicates the quality of the mirror. The central area is spherical but this is not serious because it represents a comparatively small area of glass, some of which is masked by the diagonal. The outer regions of a mirror are important because they contain the large areas of glass which play a dominant role in forming the final images. This is easily understood if we compare two mirrors, one of four inches and one of six inches diameter. The total area of the smaller is only $12\frac{1}{2}$ square inches as against the 28 square inches of the other. The area of the outer one-inch wide ring of the 6-inch mirror is $15\frac{1}{2}$ square inches, or substantially more than the whole 4-inch mirror.

The diagram has been inserted so that the reader can see for himself the figure of the 6-inch mirror which has provided all the astronomical photographs for this book. By plotting his own mirror's curve—taking the mean of a large number of separate readings with the Foucault apparatus—he should be able to judge its 'vital statistics'. Alternatively, he can wait for first-class 'seeing' conditions and test on star images. A paraboloidal mirror, submitted to the knife-edge test in the telescope, should darken evenly when the knife cuts the rays from a star at the crossover point. The full Moon appearance should darken to final extinction without differences in zonal shading showing on the glass. This is the ideal, and if the mirror presents this appearance the owner is to be congratulated. Other ways of testing mirrors in telescopes include the high-power examination of extra-focal star images on either side of the focus. Again, all these methods are fully covered in other works.[1]

As far as the telescope mirror, or objective, is concerned, the accent must be on near perfection. Upon this depend the per-

[1] Taylor, H. D. *The Adjustment and Testing of Telescope Objectives*, 4th edition, 1946.

formance and photographic results, and if the telescope's optical elements are inferior these results are bound to be disappointing.

Telescope Mountings

Assuming we have made or bought or borrowed a 6-inch mirror, what sort of tube and mounting would be most suitable for photographic work? Such a question and the way in which we attempt to answer it are beset with difficulties, and there can be no unanimous and universal agreement. My own views on the subject are not likely to meet with much support from amateurs who have perfectly good tubes and mountings built in some other way.

Having thus warned the reader, we can proceed to discuss the various types of equipment. First of all we must be sure of what we want to photograph; this has already been discussed in Chapter I, and we may decide that our first choice of objects will be the Sun, Moon and planets. All of these are found in the same strip of sky, among the zodiacal constellations. That is to say, they are seen best when due south of an observer in the northern hemisphere, and they are never to be seen near the celestial poles. Therefore, if we wish to specialize on these objects there is no need to have a telescope which can be turned to the north (or, in the case of a southern observer, to the south) celestial pole.

The really fortunate observers are those who live in the tropics, and are able to see these bodies near the zenith. They can thus observe them through the minimum thickness of atmosphere; this in itself gives these observers a considerable advantage over their northern or southern brothers.

The amateur's telescope is normally supported on one of two types of mounting. The altazimuth mounting is confined to smaller and portable instruments while the equatorial lends itself to larger and more permanent construction.

Many years ago a popular song invited the listener to '—build a stairway to the stars'. This might almost have been a lyrical invitation to construct an altazimuth mounting, for it indicates concisely the manner in which this mounting works. To follow the ascending curved path of a body between the eastern horizon and the meridian, the telescope must be moved along, then up, in a series of steps. When the body reaches the meridian, the vertical height of the step diminishes to zero. Then begins the long climb 'downstairs' towards the western horizon. The nearest the altazimuth can get to describing a curved arc in the sky, is a 'stairway' whose mean line is the star's curved path.

From the photographic standpoint this is a serious defect, as anyone who has guided a telescope will know. The visual observer —providing the instrument is equipped with smooth slow motions —can, however, accomplish much useful work.

A telescope mounted as an altazimuth instrument can only be used for photography if exposures are kept short—preferably less than one second. Guiding for long exposures is out of the question, since the telescopic field rotates at the rate of $15°$ per hour.

The overwhelming advantage of the equatorial mounting over the altazimuth is its ability to follow celestial bodies with only one movement—that of the polar axis. Whereas the two axes of an altazimuth are, respectively, vertical and horizontal, the corresponding axes of the equatorial are parallel to the Earth's axis and parallel to its equatorial plane. Unless one's observatory is situated on the equator therefore, the polar axis will have to be tilted at an angle to the horizontal. The numerical value of this angle is that of the observer's latitude.

The equatorial mounting is the only type of mounting that provides non-rotating fields. Thus all long exposures of celestial objects must be made with this type of mounting.

There is no room in this book for a long discussion of the advantages and disadvantages of the many and varied designs of equatorial mounting. But there are certain qualities that every mounting must possess, whatever type it may be.

First of all, let us spotlight some of the inherent difficulties in mounting a telescope. The most important requirement, in any and every mounting, is rigidity. A telescope focused upon a star under high magnification could be likened to a sensitive seismograph, and for this reason all obviously unsteady forms of mounting should be severely shunned. All too often one sees beautifully-machined mountings of the 'swan-neck' variety which tremble like aspen leaves in the lightest breeze.

The following, in my opinion, are of supreme importance:

(1) Rigidity.
(2) Strength.
(3) Smooth movement.

Rigidity must not be confused with strength. A mounting can be rigid without necessarily being strong, and many portable and rigid mountings have been constructed upon this principle; the Sellers[1] mounting is of this type. Nevertheless, where strength is found it is, more often than not, accompanied by rigidity. A tough, firm, solid mounting in most cases provides an unyielding and inflexible support, which allows the telescope to be pointed un-waveringly in any required direction.

Smoothly working bearings and slow motions are essential. There is nothing worse than moving parts which are jerky and stiff to turn. A stiff polar axis bearing will strain the driving clock or motor and cause wear in the worm and wheel drive. This will eventually lead to variations in the speed of the drive, causing objects to drift across the field of the telescope.

Hand-operated slow motions are essential for correcting small errors in the drive. Movements of the object due to atmospheric refraction can also be counteracted by this means. After the celestial object has been found, the telescope must be clamped and the motor will then keep it aligned on the body. All celestial objects move from east to west, completing one circuit of the star sphere in 24 sidereal hours; the Right Ascension (or Hour) circle is for this reason divided into 24 hours instead of 360°. The declination circle is divided in degrees, since Declination is measured from 0° at the celestial equator to 90° at each pole. Declination corresponds to terrestrial latitude, so that the Declination of a star at the zenith is equal to the observer's latitude.

In my early searchings for a good, solid and stable support, I tried several telescope mountings. Among them was the German

[1] Sellers, F. J. B.A.A. Journal, Vol. 62, No. 6.

type in which the telescope is supported 'out-board' at one end of the Declination axis, being counter-balanced by a weight at the other end. This sort of mounting can lack rigidity unless it is ruggedly constructed. There is a danger that the part of the declination axis which projects beyond the bearing, to which the telescope is fixed, may become a 'swan-neck'. Another disadvantage of the German form concerns the accessibility of the eyepiece which at times gets into awkward positions for the observer. On the other hand it has certain advantages: for example, it can be pointed towards all parts of the sky, in which there are no 'blind' spots.

To avoid the unsteadiness of the German mounting, I finally adopted a fork mounting closely related to the classical English mounting. In this, the telescope is swung 'inboard' between the two arms of a rugged fork and is thus supported on both sides of the tube. As long as the fork itself is solidly and rigidly mounted there is much less trouble from vibration. Furthermore the eyepiece seldom becomes inaccessible. With my mounting there is a 'blind' spot covering the north polar regions, but this is a small sacrifice to make to the goddess of stability. It is better to lose a small part of the sky completely than to see all of it imperfectly.

Another recommended mounting is the double yoke type. As with the fork, the telescope is supported on both sides, but in this case the yoke is formed by continuing the fork past the telescope trunnions to an upper bearing. Thus the yoke turns in bearings located at its northern and southern ends. The 100-inch telescope at Mt. Wilson is supported in this manner, and has a 'blind' spot in the region of the north celestial pole.

To sum up, it matters little what type of telescope mounting is used as long as it is steady and smooth-working; more important still, the operator must be aware of all its foibles.

Telescope Tubes

The problem of the telescope tube is largely a matter of personal choice, coupled with the availability of suitable materials. A gleaming and immaculate cylindrical tube may look very smart, but its performance might also be inferior to that of a roughly nailed-up square wooden tube. Many observers prefer lattice-type tubes; they are not only lighter but they provide adequate ventilation which breaks up the circulating air currents, which tend to form in closed tubes and ruin definition. Heat from the observer's body can have the same effect. Square tubes tend to check the circulation of these air currents and in stubborn cases electric fans can be beneficially employed, providing they are so mounted that no vibration is transferred to the telescope.

'Solid' type tubes are best made from some insulating material such as wood. Metal tubes are good thermal conductors, and are notorious for transmitting the observer's body-heat to the interior of the tube.

In these days of plastics and other synthetic materials, there are many alternatives available for telescope tubes. We are not limited to square tubes of wood if we prefer insulated tubes. The author's telescope tube is made from very tough resin-bonded laminated paper, and has performed exceedingly well for over ten years. It is subject to slight tube currents but these have never seriously upset observations.

In selecting suitable tube materials attention should be given to two important properties that are sometimes overlooked: the tube must not sag under its own weight, and it should not absorb water. If a tube sags under its own weight the primary mirror and the flat will move out of alignment—a serious state of affairs. Fibrous materials tend to absorb water; in so doing they also change their shape, and for this reason hardboard is not a good choice for telescope tubes. In the main it is better to avoid such substances than to try waterproofing them. These troubles are closely allied to warping and shrinkage and if a telescope tube continues to 'move' after a probationary period, it should be discarded.

All the above refers only to the tubes of reflecting telescopes, because almost without exception refracting telescopes have metal tubes. They are less troubled by tube currents, since both ends are sealed; light travels only once down the tube, and the observer's body is well away from metal of the tube.

Housings

Now let us assume we have a telescope of moderate aperture. It may be a reflector or a refractor, and is complete with suitable mounting including slow motions and a mechanical drive. What now?

Do we move all this equipment out into the garden every time we want to observe something? If so, then much valuable time is lost. I well remember manhandling my telescope and mounting out of doors in this way, only to find the sky covered with cloud by the time it had all been set up and adjusted. Under these conditions the sky automatically clears when the telescopic paraphernalia has been bundled indoors again. Having some of the equipment permanently mounted outside is a tremendous improvement, and should be attempted even if it is impossible to have a permanent abode for the complete telescope.

Many and varied are the designs for small observatories, many of them quite simple to construct. Some are completely removable from the telescope, while others have detachable roofs. In every case simplicity should be the key-note, and the sometimes difficult operating conditions (including darkness) must be kept in mind.

The observer who can build and equip a small observatory will find his efforts well rewarded. The advantages are obvious. In the first place he is able to bring his telescope quickly into action and use it more comfortably. Furthermore, the telescope objective does not have to be subjected to sudden transitions from warm to cold, and vice versa. In the absence of an observatory a telescope should be stored in the coolest room in the house. Telescope mirrors, like opera singers, are creatures of temperament and will not give of their best unless they are in the right mood. Keeping a mirror in the right mood means not subjecting it to sudden temperature changes. A mirror only gives its best performance when it is in thermal equilibrium with its surroundings. This fact should be borne in mind when the telescope is taken from the house and set up in the garden. Some few minutes must elapse before the mirror settles down, and only then can its performance be judged fairly.

Dewing occurs when the cold mirror is brought back into the warmth of the house, and must be guarded against at all costs. It is the condensation of water vapour from the air, and does not improve the mirror's aluminium or silver film. This nuisance can also happen while the telescope is in use, hence the 'dew-cap' on refractors and electric heaters for camera lenses and diagonals.

In this respect a 'solid' tube gives greater protection to a mirror than the skeleton or lattice-type tube and on no occasion has the author detected any trace of dew on his 6-inch mirror in its 'solid' tube. Diagonals are more subject to dewing, owing to their position near the open end of the telescope. In small reflecting telescopes, these mirrors contain only a few ounces of glass and can follow the temperature changes rapidly so there is less probability of dew forming upon them. Dew-caps (which are no more than extensions of the 'solid' tube) can be used, although their effect may be more psychological than physical. I must admit that I use one myself in damp, changeable weather.

Large mirrors in lattice-type tubes are most prone to condensation: being bad conductors they are unable to follow comparatively rapid changes of temperature.

There is still another advantage of a permanent observatory. The observer, being inherently lazy (like most of us) will use his telescope more often if he can go and open it up without bother, instead of having to transport his entire equipment out of doors every time he thinks of using it. Comfort and convenience to the observer are factors of some importance in the small, cold hours of the morning.

The Author's Observatory and Telescope

Some years ago I decided to build a small observatory to house my 6-inch reflector. This is lightly constructed, with a 6-foot dome of hardboard which rotates on rollers attached to laminated wooden rings. The latter were made by sawing an old 6-foot cart-wheel into two separate rings. The square structure supporting the lower fixed ring is also 6 feet along each side. An opening in the dome, 18 inches wide, is covered by a removable hardboard hatch fastened to a curved frame made from old electric conduit. Well-painted hardboard resists the weather surprisingly well.

The reason why such a small housing was constructed is simple —lack of space. In any case there is sufficient accommodation for the instrument and the observer.

So much for my 'observatory'; now for its contents. A good idea of the telescope can be obtained from the photograph (Plate I) taken several years ago, before the erection of the housing. The general lines are the same although some of the details have been changed since then.

The whole thing rests upon a great concrete 'molar' whose steel roots go deep into the clayey ground. The upper surface of this is inclined towards the north, and the cast housing containing the polar axis bearings is bolted to it. The polar axis casting contains two large ball races—one at the top, the other at the base. The whole unit is ex-radar equipment, and a small micro-wave aerial used to rotate about the top. The worm and wheel drive for the polar axis is located just under the graduated R.A. circle seen near the upper end of the casting. This end had to be slightly modified to enable the duralumin fork to be attached to the polar axis. The fork used to support an aircraft wheel during the Second World War, but seems well satisfied with its less strenuous task of supporting a 6-inch reflector. It will be noticed that the fork is slightly inclined to the polar axis. In this respect it differs from the classical English mounting and, incidentally and accidentally, allows the telescope to be pointed nearer to the north celestial pole than would otherwise be possible. Lead counterweights were fixed on a spine to balance the slightly off-axis fork and the telescope itself.

The tube swings between the two arms of the fork. The near-side bearing is split, enabling the telescope to be clamped in

Declination. There is also a manual slow motion allowing adjustment through a few degrees of Declination; this does not appear in the photograph. It is a great convenience to be able to set the telescope approximately by hand, and then to make the final adjustment by means of the slow motion. The Declination circle is attached to the cradle holding the telescope tube.

The tough resin-bonded tube has already been referred to. This, the fork and the radar mounting were all obtained very cheaply from a local scrap dealer. Likewise the mirror cell and its supporting metal flange.

The mirror cell is of sufficient thickness to allow the mirror to be partially sunk into it. A metal ring retains the mirror in place. The performance of a telescope mirror depends, in no small way, on the manner in which it is mounted. Before condemning a mirror for its inability to give clearly defined star images, a careful examination of the cell should be made. Any strain on the glass or tightness in the fit of the cell will certainly upset definition. My mirror rests on several thicknesses of blotting paper, which just bring it up to the correct height. The retaining ring exerts practically no pressure on the mirror.

This point is very important. The mirror must be so supported in its cell that, no matter what the position of the telescope, it will not be subjected to undue or uneven pressure. Mirrors, like feet, show their discomfort when they are confined in tight containers.

The upper end of the telescope tube houses the diagonal, which is supported centrally on four thin vanes of steel. These produce a cruciform diffraction pattern superimposed symmetrically on the images of bright stars; three vanes produce six-armed patterns. Such patterns are formed at the expense of image brightness and contrast, but the diagonal must be supported somehow, and even a single robust support will produce diffraction 'spikes' on both sides of a star image.

With the telescope pointed towards the south, the eyepiece is on the eastern side of the tube. A little above it is the small telescope which acts as a finder. Cameras used for celestial photography are fixed to the eyepiece draw-tube. Rack and pinion adjustment is not

1. The author's 6-inch reflecting telescope.

2. Two views of author's 35 mm. astronomical camera.

Top: Showing the back, and the 'keyhole cover' removed to reveal the focusing eyepiece. The white plastic is a writing tablet on which relevant data can be recorded with a pencil.

Below: With the L-shaped back removed; the spools and frame-block are clearly shown.

really essential but I have always found that little refinements such as this make for easier working conditions.

It will be noticed from the photograph that the polar axis bearing is not actually seated on the concrete pier, but rests on four steel bolts protruding from it. This is to facilitate the adjustment of the polar axis, since it would have been impossible to cast the upper, inclined face of the concrete pier with the requisite degree of precision. The whole ensemble really rests upon four adjustable steel bolts; when the correct setting of the polar axis had been found, it was secured by locking nuts screwed down on their bolts.

The method used for adjusting the polar axis was the time-honoured one of sighting the telescope on three well-separated stars of the same, or very nearly the same, Declination. When they all, in turn, appear in the field of a medium power eyepiece, as the polar axis is rotated, the axis cannot be far out of adjustment. (Stars too close to the horizon should not be used, because of the effects of atmospheric refraction.)

A clamp is attached to the toothed wheel driving the polar axis, so that the telescope can either be swung freely in Right Ascension or locked to the axis, when the drive will cause it to follow a selected object. Ball-race bearings move, if anything, too easily, and it was found necessary to introduce some additional friction in the polar axis bearing. A piece of flat, springy phosphor-bronze was mounted on the lower end of the polar axis so that it rubbed against the lower ball-race cradle as the axis rotated. This introduced enough friction, and the telescope could be left unclamped despite small off-balance effects.

One or two odd items may be briefly mentioned. First, a cover like a saucepan lid fits snugly over the mirror retaining ring when the telescope is not in use, protecting the mirror from dust, dirt and dew; it contains a few sheets of blotting paper to absorb moisture. A similar cover, fitting over the upper end of the tube, keeps out dust and protects the diagonal.

The drive is supplied by a 50-cycle synchronous motor, connected to the mains. Spur gears are used for the earlier stages of speed reduction, the final drive being relayed to the polar axis by

65

E

sprocket wheels and a chain to the worm. There is also a manually-operated slow motion in Right Ascension (consisting of a differential gear) for guiding the telescope during photographic work, allowing any slight irregularities in the drive to be corrected.

Telescope Drives and the Lunar Rate

Here is a word of warning to the beginner in astronomy. Suspect the man who tries to sell you a motor or clock drive for maintaining a telescope at the lunar rate. There is no such thing as 'the' lunar rate, and no simple device can keep the Moon indefinitely within the field of a telescope.

The apparent rate of the Moon's motion among the stars is in fact subject to considerable variations. These depend not only on the day-to-day changes due to the ellipticity of the lunar orbit but also, more markedly, on the hour-to-hour changes produced by the observer's motion in relation to the Moon, giving to the latter an apparent velocity much lower near meridian passage than when it is near either horizon.

Nevertheless it is quite possible to install a driving mechanism (or modify the sidereal drive by suitable gearing) so that the telescope will follow the Moon in Right Ascension for fairly long periods without recourse being had to the slow motions.

CHAPTER 4

Cameras and Accessories

Ordinary cameras

Cameras are many and varied, ranging from lilliputian to truly gargantuan dimensions. The expensive ones are invariably more versatile, and incorporate all sorts of additional gadgetry. The simplest one of all is a pin-hole camera. It is essentially a light-tight box with a small hole pierced at one end; rays of light admitted through this fall upon a piece of photographic emulsion at the other end. No lens is used, and focusing is unnecessary. The image is inverted as in conventional cameras.

A camera is defined as an instrument in which photographic materials are exposed to light under controlled conditions. It has four main parts:

(1) A light-tight box.
(2) An image forming device—lenses or mirrors.
(3) Plate or film holders; (in the case of roll film, spools).
(4) A shutter for controlling exposures.

For the purposes of this book a conventional or 'ordinary' camera is an instrument in which the focal plane images are formed on the photographic emulsion by a positive or converging lens of short focal length. In such a camera the short focal length of the lens—seldom more than a few inches in portable equipment—permits a wide field of view which allows the photographic emulsion to record widely separated objects. A wide field of view is obtained at the expense of fine detail because the photographic images of distant objects are small and much of the finer structure is lost in emulsion diffusion. Field coverage and definition depend solely on the quality of the camera lens which, in a simple box camera, may be a single meniscus lens, or, in an expensive instrument, a large aperture multi-element lens combination especially computed to give excellent wide angle definition over a standard plate area. The Kodak Aero-Ektar, the Ross Wide Angle Xpres and the Dallmeyer Pentac are three examples of wide angle lenses which, since the Second World War, have been used by amateur astronomers who specialize in meteor and comet work and other forms of celestial photography where large areas of sky are involved. These lenses are essentially 'light gatherers' and they enable astronomers to use much shorter exposures than are necessary with smaller aperture lenses of similar focal length.

An excellent large aperture lens focuses star images as minute discs over the entire area of the photographic plate; also, with such a lens, the developed images of extended objects are small and concentrated often at the expense of fine detail.

Guiding a short focus camera

It has long been the custom to mount a short focal length wide aperture camera on a larger telescope of greater focal length and, using the latter as a guiding telescope, make long exposures at the night sky. My own 6-inch reflector tube is saddled with a small wooden platform fixed symmetrically above the declination axis, and this supports cameras which are from time to time clamped to it.

A suitable star is selected near the centre of the photographic field and the telescope is guided on it. To facilitate this operation it is usual to employ thickish cross-wires (thin ones are difficult to see at night) and a high-power eyepiece which is racked a little out of focus so that the star image appears as an enlarged disc of light. It is the task of the astronomical photographer to observe this disc and keep it centrally displayed on the cross-wires, and this is more easily accomplished if the telescope is rigidly mounted and smoothly driven by a clock or electric motor, and it is essential that it should be equipped with manual slow motion controls so that he can make small corrections in Right Ascension and

Declination. In this manner a small amount of 'run-off' can be seen and corrected before image displacements become serious in the camera.

It is not my intention to deal with this sort of photography in great detail; the methods are fully described in other books. There are, however, several important points which deserve mention: firstly, a large aperture wide angle lens is very 'fast' in the photographic sense and this means that it is highly sensitive to stray light which can be brighter, in some cases, than the celestial objects the operator wishes to record. For this reason, during a photographic session, a careful watch must be kept for the effects of scattered moonlight, street lighting and other sources of illumination whose light will fog the sensitive emulsion.

Secondly, a beginner may be tempted to use the fastest emulsions for long exposures on the sky in the hope of recording fainter objects, but, by so doing, he would be overlooking the effects of reciprocity failure which makes these emulsions most unsuitable for this type of work. On the other hand, they are well suited for meteor (and artificial satellite) work for they are able to record easily the bright trails across the night sky at the expense of fainter objects which, on more moderately speeded emulsions, would become too obtrusive. Stationary cameras are preferred for this work.

Lastly, a large aperture wide angle lens must be protected from water which will condense on it if the surrounding air becomes warmer than the glass. Dew on the glass surfaces can make a lens almost opaque, and it is usual to provide protection in the form of a dew-cap, an insulated tubular extension of the lens cell, which may contain a low wattage electric heater to warm the outer glass surface that is most prone to condensation.

So much for the shorter focal length cameras with their wide fields and small image scales. Since the image size is proportional to the focal length of the lens which forms it, the short focal length lens on the camera must be replaced by one of longer focal length if proportionately larger focal plane images are to fall on the emulsion. At the same time, this restricts the field presented to the plate and this can only be restored by increasing proportionately the size of the photographic plate which, in most cases, is undesirable and cannot be done without rebuilding the camera.

Using the telescope objective as a camera lens

The amateur must be prepared to sacrifice large angular fields in his astronomical camera if he wishes to obtain enlarged whole disc negatives of the Sun and Moon. A lens which will give excellent definition over an angular field of 2° or 3° is more than adequate, and this performance is well up to that of a good telescope objective which can be substituted for the camera lens. From the practical point of view it is the telescope which becomes the camera, and the problem is to place a piece of photographic emulsion precisely in the focal plane which is always to be found in the draw-tube. Also, since the photographic emulsion needs some form of protection against stray light, it is usual to enclose it in a box which can be fitted to the draw-tube by means of an adaptor. The box, which can be called a camera attachment, must be fitted with a slide or shutter so that the photographic emulsion is kept in complete darkness until an exposure is attempted.

Using the telescope mirror for photography

In precisely the same way a piece of photographic emulsion can be placed at the Newtonian focus of a reflecting telescope where it will receive sharply focused images from the mirror. In this case the camera plugs into the draw-tube which, on the Newtonian, is situated at the upper end of the telescope tube.

Refractors and reflectors are thus converted into powerful astronomical cameras and they are able to produce sizable images of extended objects. On account of its smaller focal ratio the average reflector is nearly four times as fast as the average refractor, which gives the reflector a considerable advantage when faint objects are to be recorded.

Using the normal telescope with an ordinary camera

An astronomical telescope in normal adjustment projects parallel light rays from the eyepiece into the observer's eye, and these are focused on to the retina which lies in the focal plane of the lens in a perfect eye. The eye is in fact a small camera and it is a simple task to replace it at the eyepiece with an 'ordinary' camera containing film; any of the smaller wide aperture cameras are suitable for this task: nothing is gained by using a large lens for only a small central area of it would be used, and the weight would complicate the problem of supporting it.

Before making an exposure the camera is focused to infinity and then pointed squarely at the telescope eyepiece. The shutter is released without introducing vibration.

One advantage of this method is that neither the telescope nor the camera need be modified in any way, and the observer can change quickly from visual to photographic work. The main drawbacks are associated with light losses in the large number of glass lenses involved and the poor definition away from the centre of the field. Some of my own experiments with this method are described later in this chapter. Galilean telescopes, in normal adjustment, can also be used in this way.

Using the telescope and a camera without a lens

Parallel rays projected from the positive eyepiece of a normally-adjusted telescope are transformed into converging rays when the eyepiece is racked in, and these can be brought to focus a few inches behind the telescope to yield highly enlarged images of celestial objects. Image scale is set by the power of the eyepiece and its distance from the focusing screen; a large distance causes a large diluted image to be formed. With this arrangement the telescope objective (or mirror) forms focal plane images which are enlarged in the same way as those of a lantern slide. No additional camera lenses are used.

The usable angular field is small and variable, according to the

71

power of the eyepiece; focal ratios of $f/50$ to $f/100$ are commonly employed, and effective focal lengths are very great. A telescope adjusted in this way with a photographic plate arranged to receive the highly enlarged images makes an efficient camera for lunar close-ups and planetary work. Again some sort of camera attachment (or camera minus its lens) must be fixed squarely beyond the eyepiece if fine work is to be done.

A Galilean telescope employs a simple negative eyepiece which, in normal adjustment, is arranged to deliver parallel rays of light into the observer's eye. Refractors and reflectors function as Galilean telescopes when the positive eyepieces are replaced by negative ones, although practical considerations sometimes make such exchanges difficult. Galilean eyepieces have optical properties which are similar to those of the Barlow lens which is described later in this chapter.

This type of telescope can be used for photographic work and, if the negative eyepiece is racked out a little, images are formed which, though inverted, resemble those formed by the positive eyepiece. The camera is attached to the draw-tube as before. Image sizes, focal ratios and effective focal lengths are smaller, and angular fields are larger, for this type of eyepiece is less powerful than the positive eyepieces.

The important differences between the various types of equipment are summarized in the table on page 73 opposite.

TYPE OF APPARATUS	SUITABLE OBJECTS	ANGULAR FIELD	IMAGE MAGNIFICATION	FOCAL RATIO	EFFECTIVE FOCAL LENGTH	EXPOSURE DURATION
Short focus wide angle camera	Star fields Comets Nebulae Meteors, etc.	Large. More than 40°	Very small	Very small $f/2$–$f/4$	Very short: not variable	Very short
Reflector with plate at Newtonian focus	Whole disc Sun & Moon. Close star clusters. Comets. Nebulae	Small: restricted by draw-tube & flat	Moderate	Small $f/6$–$f/10$	Short: not variable	Short
Refractor with plate at prime focus	Whole disc Sun & Moon	Small: restricted by draw-tube	Moderate	$f/15$	Short: not variable	Too long for faint objects
Reflector or refractor with eyepiece[1] & camera with lens	Portions Sun & Moon. Planets.	Small: marginal images poor	Variable depending on eyepiece[1] & camera[2] lens	Large and variable	Large and variable	Moderate depending on f/ratio
Reflector or refractor with eyepiece[3] & camera without lens	Highly enlarged portions of Sun & Moon. Close-ups of planets	Very small: minutes of arc	Very large & variable	Very large & variable	Very large & variable	Long depending on f/ratio

[1] The eyepiece, in this case, can be a high or low power positive, or a low power Galilean type.
[2] The focal length of the camera lens affects image size. (see Appendix A.)
[3] A Barlow lens can be used instead of a positive eyepiece for lower magnifications.

73

Constructional considerations

In assembling a camera attachment certain constructional requirements must be considered:

(1) Weight.

(2) Rigidity.

(3) Method of attachment to the telescope.

Taking (1) first, a heavy camera will upset the balance of the telescope. In the case of the reflecting telescope, the camera will be near the top of the tube and counterweights can be fixed to its lower end. Small bags containing lead-shot may be hooked on, or the operator might prefer a more permanent arrangement, consisting of a weight sliding on a metal rod held to the tube by two small brackets. If the camera is mounted on the ocular draw-tube, excessive weight may distort the draw-tube fittings.

Rigidity, (2), is equally important if the telescopic images, particularly during long exposures, are to remain accurately aligned on the emulsion.

As regards (3), my own telescope can be switched from visual work to photography in a matter of seconds, simply by plugging the camera into the draw-tube. Such haste may not be absolutely essential, but there is no need to go to the opposite extreme, which requires spanners and screwdrivers when making this transition. Grazed knuckles and torn fingers sometimes accompany such operations when they are attempted in difficult lighting. The accent should, as always, be on simplicity.

Focusing and Photography with Simple Apparatus

Pictures of the Moon can be taken without a camera and will show some detail. The method, while not recommended for serious work, is useful in underlining certain important principles. Apparatus needed (in addition to the telescope) includes a metal knife-edge, a piece of cardboard more than large enough to cover the upper end of the telescope, and a slow glass photographic plate.

The method is simple. The telescope is pointed at a bright star not too far away from the Moon; the eyepiece is removed and the observer looks down the draw-tube. If the star has been correctly centred, the mirror will be full of its light, and will look to the observer something like a very dim full Moon. The eyepiece draw-tube must be capable of precise adjustment; the knife-edge is now placed almost diametrically across its open end, and held there firmly so that the converging starlight passes it before entering the observer's eye. The Foucault knife-edge test is now applied by advancing the knife-edge across the end of the draw-tube until it intercepts the cone of light. If the movement of the knife-edge results in a black shadow crossing the evenly illuminated mirror in the same direction as the knife-edge, the draw-tube should be racked out a little. If the shadow advances in the opposite direction to the knife-edge, the draw-tube should be racked in. At the correct setting it is impossible to tell which way the shadows are crossing, for the mirror will darken evenly all over, as though the star were itself being dimmed. The edge of the draw-tube now coincides with the focal plane of the mirror. If we now point the instrument at the Moon, taking care to get the image centrally placed in the draw-tube, photography can be started. The upper end of the telescope is covered with the cardboard disc, and the knife-edge is replaced by the photographic plate, which is pressed against the end of the draw-tube. With a large plate several attempts can be made, providing there are no very bright artificial lights near the telescope. The exposure is made by the quick removal and replacement of the cardboard covering the end of the telescope. All vibration must be avoided if good results are to be secured; to this end, four hands are better than two, one person holding the plate and the other operating the shutter. Slow plates can be handled in the light of the full Moon for short periods without fear of fogging.

Some improvement on the above method is obviously desirable, and to facilitate this a plate attachment can be constructed. In its simplest form, this consists of a piece of flat wood or metal with guides fixed to one side, between which a plateholder can be slipped. Mounted on the other side is a standard threaded or parallel tubular adaptor which fits into the eyepiece draw-tube. The part of the wood or metal plate at the bottom of this tube is cut away. With the loaded plate-holder in place, the protective slide is withdrawn and the plate exposed by removing and replacing the cardboard shutter as before. Focusing by the knife-edge method can only be successful if the plane of the photographic emulsion is coincident with that of the knife-edge, and to achieve this requires a little care. One way is to sacrifice a spare plate-holder and attach the knife-edge permanently to it; other and more ingenious ways will suggest themselves to the practising amateur. Whichever way is finally adopted, the emphasis must be on accuracy.

Plate-holders

The plate-holder is really a shallow box with a sliding light-tight lid; its job is to keep the photographic plate in darkness until we want to expose it. Metal and wooden plate-holders are in everyday use and, while they are reckoned to be light-tight, quite a percentage of them are not. It is tempting fate to take loaded plate-holders out into strong sunlight without suitable protection around them. This precaution is also an insurance against fogged emulsions in loaded cameras; it costs nothing and can save considerable disappointment.

Plate-holders slide into a camera attachment from one end and fit snugly against it. Slits which admit light are sealed by black velvet or similar material; alternatively, the whole ensemble can be protected by a black cloth.

Other Focusing Methods

Assuming that the operator has some idea of where the focal plane of his objective is with regard to his camera attachment, he can load a plate-holder and find the correct focus by trial and error. The telescope need not be driven and any bright star makes a suitable target; a finder will be found useful for recovering the

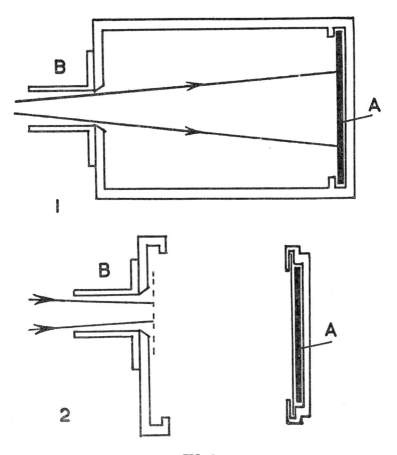

FIG. 4

Simple cameras for (1) enlarged and (2) focal plane images.

In both instances A *and* B *represent the photographic plate and draw-tube adaptor respectively.*

In 1, *the draw-tube adaptor can house the enlarging eyepiece, or it can be plugged into a draw-tube already containing an enlarging eyepiece. The camera body may be of wood.*

The apparatus in 2 *consists of a plate-holder sliding into the supporting frame attached to the draw-tube adaptor. The latter is purposely off-centred in respect of the photographic plate so as to enable two sequences to be recorded on one plate. This is readily accomplished by reversing the plate-holder in the frame.*

star after each exposure. Briefly, the idea is to allow the star image to trail across an identifiable part of the plate. Each exposure is made at a slightly different focusing position, and is carefully marked and noted. A scribed line on the draw-tube where it emerges from the outer fixed tube is one way of marking its setting. As several star trails may be recorded on the same piece of emulsion, resulting in possible confusion, blanks should be inserted on them. This is done by closing the end of the telescope at fixed intervals. Thus trail No. 1, with no blanking marks, is associated with position No. 1. Trail No. 2 with 5-second blanking marks corresponds to position No. 2, and so on.

Having done this, it is only necessary, after development, to find the setting which gives the sharpest and thinnest star trail. This is marked clearly and accurately on the draw-tube, so that it can easily be found again. There are various ways of doing this. Assuming the camera to be plugged into the draw-tube to a definite and reproducible setting, a deep cut can be made with a penknife on the draw-tube where it emerges from the fixed outer tube. Other ways include the drilling of a tiny hole through both tubes, or the fitting of adjustable collars on the draw-tube itself. In the former case, the correct setting is found by poking the plain end of the drill through both holes.

Ground glass screens are used for ordinary photographic focusing, but owing to the coarse nature of the ground surface they are not really suitable for celestial photography, where it is customary to examine the images with a magnifying lens. Nevertheless, such screens are not entirely valueless, and in the absence of other means they can be used to good effect. Like the knife-edge they must be arranged to slide into the camera attachment, and care must be taken to ensure accurate registration with the plane of the photographic emulsion. The accurate focus can be found with a magnifying glass or a low power positive eyepiece.

If there is no means of magnifying the ground glass images there is another method I have used successfully on occasion. First, the telescope is pointed at a bright star whose image is allowed to fall on the ground glass. The observer's eye is then brought up fairly close to the back of the screen—about half an inch will do; the distance is not critical. The star image is seen as a large round disc of light. If it is focused precisely on the ground glass, it will have a sharply defined edge; unfocused images will have ill-defined edges, and the position of the draw-tube must be adjusted until the edges are sharply defined. Do not try to focus the eye on the screen—keep it quite relaxed.

An undeveloped, fixed and washed fine-grain photographic plate makes a better focusing screen than a piece of ground glass. A fine-grain focusing screen can also be made from a glass plate etched with the fumes of hydrofluoric acid. (A word of warning here: do not attempt to use this acid, but let an expert do it. Hydrofluoric acid is dangerous.)

Accuracy in focusing must be our obsession. Other photographic workers can 'stop down', a process which gives them considerable latitude in focusing, but we cannot afford to do this since it reduces the speed and resolution of our telescope. The utmost care and attention must be lavished on this most important operation. Other processes have at least some latitude—an under- or over-exposed negative can be 'doctored' to yield reasonable results and graininess can be minimized to some extent, but if the negative is out of focus there is nothing we can do to correct it.

Shutters

Shutters found in amateur hands usually fall under one of three headings:

(1) Flap-type shutters for closing the upper end of the telescope.
(2) Metal-leaved shutters of the diaphragm type.
(3) Focal-plane or roller-blind-type shutters.

There are others, but these are the popular ones. Flap shutters, which we have already met, can be constructed of any stiff, light-tight material: cardboard, hardboard and plywood immediately suggest themselves as being both suitable and cheap. Thick black cloth on a lightly made frame will also serve; endless possibilities present themselves for the manufacture of this type of shutter.

79

In operation, this type of shutter is held over the mouth of the telescope tube so that no light can enter. A few seconds before making an exposure, the shutter should be edged away just clear of the tube to allow telescope vibration to cease. The exposure is made by quickly moving the shutter sideways and replacing it again. Even if the exposure duration is several seconds, both movements of the shutter should be rapid, and needless to say it must be well clear of the tube during the exposure.

In my opinion the fastest exposure obtainable with this type of shutter is about 1/5 of a second—but this must vary to some extent from one individual to another. When faster exposures are needed another type of shutter must be used. Such a shutter would be an oblong screen, wider than the aperture of the telescope, with an open central portion whose width is the same as the aperture. Before exposure, one end of the screen completely covers the mouth of the tube. The exposure is made by moving the screen rapidly across the tube mouth, so that the mirror is flooded with light as the open centre section of the screen passes. After the exposure the tube is light-sealed by the other end of the screen. There is no one correct way of doing this, providing absolute freedom from vibration is secured.

Lattice and open-type telescope tubes are naturally more prone to the effects of stray light from nearby lamps and houses. If this is incident to the axis of the draw-tube and the open camera, fogging of the emulsion may occur. This can be eliminated by fixing a piece of black cloth or blackened cardboard to the opposite side of the tube. With this in place, cardboard flap-type shutters can be used without trouble at night.

Another way of ensuring protection from stray light is to employ other types of camera shutters either on the draw-tube or on the camera itself. The upper end of the telescope can then be left to its own devices. Let us consider the metal-leaved, diaphragm type of shutter found in the lens assembly of ordinary commercial cameras. The circular shutter housing contains three or more metal leaves which combine to cover the aperture; these are hinged and can be set to open and shut at predetermined speeds.

80

Depending on the make of shutter there is either a rotating ring or a knob for setting the speeds. Usually, a built-in iris diaphragm forms part of the assembly, but in our work this will normally be kept wide open. It is common practice to mount the shutter between the front and back components of the camera lens, so that the rays of light from the object are cut at their narrowest point.

In some of the older shutters, exposures can be made repeatedly by merely pressing the release, since the operating springs are always under tension—a fact which does not always improve their performance. Nevertheless I have used such shutters quite satisfactorily.

Other, more modern shutters—such as the famous Compur—embody levers which have to be set to tension the springs. Thus the springs are relaxed when the shutter is not in use; this helps to maintain the stated, but often inaccurate, speeds.

Shutters made to fit on the fronts of portrait and studio cameras are available in large sizes. Their speeds are usually fairly slow—up to about 1/50 of a second. Some of these are operated by pneumatic bulbs. Others, like most of the between-the-lens type, use a cable release. These enable shutters to be operated without vibration—an important point.

Focal-plane shutters, sometimes called roller-blind shutters, normally operate close to the surface of the photographic emulsion. Expensive cameras with interchangeable lenses—the Leica is a famous example—use these shutters which are essentially similar to the slotted, flap-type shutter described above. A narrow slot in a rubberized blind scans the emulsion from top to bottom, exposing it to the image in the focal plane. The first portion or strip of emulsion 'sees' the object before subsequent strips—in normal work with fast-moving objects this sometimes leads to peculiar distortions.

One important advantage of the focal-plane shutter over the metal-leaved type is its ability to expose all parts of the emulsion equally. This advantage is most noticeable with exposures shorter than 1/50 of a second. With metal-leaved type shutters, instead of

81

F

one smooth action, there are two actions—the opening and the shutting. The shutter opens from the centre and light is admitted in this region before the metal leaves are fully open. When the shutter closes, the central portion is left until last; thus the centre of the plate is given a longer exposure than the edges. With ordinary cameras the shutter is mounted between the lens components minimizing the effect which is most objectionable when the shutter is close to the focal plane. It is not necessary to work with high speeds much of the time—solar work is the one exception. At lower speeds, when the opening and shutting intervals are small fractions of the total exposure time, metal-leaved type shutters perform well even if they are outside the lens, or in our case, the eyepiece housing.

Shutters for astronomical work should have ample aperture ensuring complete coverage of the photographic emulsions. Sometimes the corners of a plate are found to be under-exposed; this effect is known as 'vignetting' and is due to something—not necessarily the shutter—partially obtruding between the light source and the emulsion. The lens mountings themselves may be the culprits.

Metal-leaved and focal-plane shutters are not simple to construct and are often expensive to purchase. They may sometimes be discovered at camera club 'junk' sales and the like.

Here then are two ideas for those readers who might like to experiment with home-made shutters.

A thin circular disc of metal pivoted in the middle has a radial slot cut in one side of it. As the wheel-like disc rotates, the slot scans an opening and admits light into the camera. The faster it rotates—the quicker the exposure. Coiled helical springs, like those from the cheaper clockwork toys, drive the shutter. A ratchet tooth filed on the outer periphery can be made to engage with a releasing lever. After each exposure the spring will have 'run down' a little and some means must be included for resetting it—or, as long as the upper end of the telescope is covered, the shutter can be turned back—which will achieve the same object.

Another shutter like the above employs a spiral slot instead of a radial one. This is the principle of the Nipkow disc, the spiral slot scanning the open aperture; its action, from the emulsion's point of view, resembles that of the focal-plane shutter.

Plates v. Film

Whether to use plates or film must be left to the discretion of the individual. His decision will automatically influence the design and construction of the camera and associated parts. It will therefore be worth while to devote a little space to this all-important problem.

Taking plates first, we may tabulate their disadvantages as follows:

(1) Fragility.
(2) High cost.
(3) Difficulty in handling—coupled with manipulating plate holders in poor light.
(4) Storage.

(1) and (2) need little amplification; whether or not plates are considered expensive rests with the individual.

(3)—protective slides covering the plates seem to sense when they are in poor light and sometimes tend to jam and stick, to the chagrin of the operator. It has been said that the night air affects sliding covers, particularly on wooden plate-holders—certainly humidity might be a contributory cause. Much depends upon the design of plate-holder and the adroitness of the operator. If the sliding plate cover is pulled too far open it is likely to leave the grooves and there may be some difficulty in replacing it. Then there is the operation of removing and replacing plate-holders— grooves are again involved and their manipulation may bedevil the photographer. Practice can do much to alleviate such troubles, and complete familiarity with his apparatus must be one of the photographer's first aims.

The smallest standard English plate is $2\frac{1}{2} \times 3\frac{1}{2}$ inches. Smaller sizes than this are sometimes made for specialized work, or

83

again, larger plates can be cut by the amateur himself with a glass cutter. In essence, the process consists of ruling a straight and continuous cut across the glass. Opinions may differ as to the correct way of carrying out this tricky operation. I personally prefer to lay the plate, emulsion downwards, on a clean, flat, paper-covered surface; this, at least, ensures that the cutting operation does not start off by scratching the emulsion. A steel rule is held firmly across the plate and the cut is made with one movement of the wheel or diamond. The operator can easily tell when the tool is biting into the surface by the hissing noise it makes. The plate is then reversed and held by the thumbs and forefingers of both hands by the side nearest the operator. The rest of the plate stretches away from him, the line of the cut separating the two sets of fingers and thumbs. The action of breaking the plate along the cut is carried out by slightly forcing the centre of the plate downwards. It should then be possible to fold the two upper emulsion-coated surfaces together on a hinge of gelatin.

When cutting plates one's chief care must be for the emulsion; if this is damaged, all is lost. Emulsions are sensitive to mechanical pressure, which may produce unsightly markings on the developed plate. Blue-sensitive and orthochromatic plates can be cut in the glow of red safelights. Panchromatic plates must be cut in total darkness and templates can be constructed to facilitate this.

Having digressed slightly and, it is hoped, helpfully, we can proceed to the question of storage, (4). It is little use going to great trouble and expense processing good plates if they are to be ruined in storage. They can be stored in the original boxes, emulsion to emulsion, separated by thin pieces of paper at the sides. This might seem to be the answer, until we contemplate trying to extricate one of the middle ones: if for some reason we wish to inspect a negative, we do not want to disturb all the adjacent ones. A better way of storing them is in long slotted walled boxes like lantern slide containers. Each plate has its own numbered compartment from which it can be removed without upsetting its fellows.

It is only fair to state the advantages of plates, though in my opinion these do not offset the disadvantages for the amateur. The main advantages are:

(1) Extreme flatness as compared with film.

(2) Rigid glass base—not influenced by humidity or thermal effects.

(3) Small gelatin shifts—important for accurate measurements.

(4) Greater number of emulsions.

Of these, (3) is particularly important to the professional astronomer, much of whose work involves the accurate measuring of photographic images.

Regarding (4) emulsions can be obtained covering the whole range from ultra-violet to the far infra-red; this gives the plate user certain advantages over the 35mm. enthusiast.

So much, then, for photographic plates. What of film? Cut film can be obtained in large sizes like plates but here I shall only discuss spooled 35mm. film. First let us enumerate the advantages of this material:

(1) Non-fragility.

(2) Low cost.

(3) Easy manipulation with winding knobs.

(4) Small size suitable for planetary work.

The disadvantages can best be shown by comparing film with plates:

(1) Lack of extreme flatness.

(2) Non-rigid base which can buckle and stretch.

(3) Gelatin shifts combine with (2) to reduce the accuracy of measurements.

(4) Restricted range of emulsions—notably of infra-red in Great Britain.

Film cannot be made to lie optically flat, but it can be made to lie flat enough for our purposes. Regarding (2) and (3) there will certainly be some stretching of the film and displacement of the gelatin, but this is not likely to be considerable enough to affect the work of the amateur.

35mm. film can be bought in various lengths from the 5ft.

(1·6m) 'reloads' to many feet, according to requirements. Panchromatic emulsions are the most common, and range from slow, contrasty and grainless ones to extremely fast, 'soft' and grainy ones. In recent years the oscilloscope has come into such general use that special emulsions have been developed for the sole purpose of recording the elusive blue and green traces of the cathode-ray tube, so that the astronomical photographer can now add 35mm. high-speed blue-sensitive and ortho-emulsions to his armoury. Other films include the costly infra-red, and the film-strip positive emulsions.

Commercial Cameras

Commercial cameras can be used for astronomical work and the owner of a Leica or any 35mm. camera with removable or interchangeable lenses can soon adapt it for telescopic requirements. They are often expensive, however, and not everyone can afford to spend perhaps several hundred pounds on a camera of this type. Even a second-hand camera body without a lens can cost £30 or more. The cheaper models normally have built-in lenses and shutters of the metal-leaved type.

The simplest way of obtaining pictures of celestial objects is to point the camera into the eyepiece of the already focused telescope and press the shutter release. The telescope should be focused for normal vision and the camera lens set at infinity.

The drawback of this method is the difficulty of pressing the shutter release without introducing vibration. Vibration will ruin any exposure and cannot be tolerated. Alternatively, the camera may be mounted on a platform or bracket fixed to the telescope, an ordinary wire release being used for triggering the shutter.

My own experiments with this type of photography were made with a Voigtlander Vito II. The shutter housing contains, among other things, the famous Color-Skopar lens and a delayed action device. The latter enables the shutter to be triggered manually but not instantaneously, several seconds elapsing before the

86

exposure is made. Thus the camera can be held steady while the shutter is released by the clockwork delayed action mechanism.

This arrangement with a low power eyepiece and fast film is capable of yielding good views of the centre of the field, but off-axial images suffer since the definition is not good near the edges. As we have seen already, there may be serious loss of light due to the large number of glass components in the system. My own eye-piece consists of two cemented doublets, while the Color Skopar is a four-element lens. In this particular lens all surfaces are bloomed or coated to reduce light losses due to reflection, but with un-bloomed lenses the loss of light can be quite appreciable.

An amateur equipped with a reflecting telescope and this type of camera, and without other apparatus, should persevere with this method—it would be instructive, for instance, to see just how much fine lunar detail could be recorded.

The more fortunate possessor of a camera with a removable objective is able to make, or have made, an adaptor for it. This replaces the lens and is machined to fit snugly into the draw-tube. If the camera is of the single-lens reflex type so much the better, for then the viewer can be used both to focus the image and to ensure that the object to be photographed really is within the field of the camera. This constitutes a problem in non-reflex type cameras, whose solution is to mount a finder on the tube of the main telescope. The greater the finder's focal length the better. The exact placing of the image becomes increasingly difficult as higher magnifications are used, and a small error may lead to the image missing the camera aperture completely.

A finder of adequate focal length is also useful in selecting the best moments of seeing, prior to exposing. Due to the usually rapid changes of our atmosphere, the choice of the best moment to expose is often difficult. In my opinion an $f/15$ 3-inch refractor would be an admirable guide telescope for a 6-inch.

A 35mm. Astronomical Camera

The problem of finding the precise focus can be attacked in any of the various ways already described. It was this very problem that prompted me to design my own 35mm. astro-camera[1] some years ago. Since then, hundreds of feet of film have passed through it; results have been good and I can confidently recommend this type of construction.

First a word about the method of focusing adopted in this camera. To focus a telescope means to adjust the focal plane of the eyepiece till it coincides with that of the objective. If the focused telescope is pointing at a star, there will be an aerial image of that star in the draw-tube. This image is quite independent of the eyepiece, and if the latter is removed the image can be made to fall upon a focusing screen. Or again, it could impinge upon the photographic emulsion.

In my camera, a positive eyepiece is permanently focused upon the plane normally occupied by the emulsion. The operation of focusing the camera thus moves the eyepiece and film in relation to the telescope but not to each other. Since the focal plane of the eyepiece coincides with that of the emulsion, it follows that an image which is sharply defined in the eyepiece will also be sharply defined upon the emulsion. The film is loaded and a small hole is punched in it. A high-power positive eyepiece is mounted on the back of the camera and locked in such a position that it is sharply focused on the plane of the emulsion. To focus the camera, all that the observer has to do is look through the eyepiece, the punched hole in the film and the open shutter into the telescope. He then racks the whole camera in or out until a sharply defined image is seen in the positive eyepiece, and he can be confident that it will also be in perfect focus upon the film.

Negative eyepieces cannot be used for this work: their focal planes lie between the lenses, so that they cannot focus on anything outside themselves; all positive eyepieces (such as Ramsdens and orthoscopics) on the other hand, have external focal planes. Some difficulty may be encountered regarding the choice of a suitable eyepiece: $\frac{1}{4}$ inch focal length is adequate, but not all of such eyepieces can be placed close enough to the film, on account

---

[1] Rackham, T. W. *B.A.A. Journal*, Vol. 66, No. 2.

of their metal mountings. Failing the complete removal of the lens unit from the brass-work, some alternative must be sought. Suitable lenses are sometimes to be found in Government-surplus stores. Old-fashioned microscope objectives—a quarter-inch (focal length) being quite a modest power—will also perform well as focusing eyepieces, without drastic modification.

Precise adjustment of the focal plane of the eyepiece to that of the emulsion is of paramount importance—the success or failure of the whole procedure depends on it. A piece of clear, exposed film, with a few scratches on its emulsion side, is employed for this purpose; it must be long enough to stretch across its supporting block and supply a few turns on the spools at either side; short pieces may not assume the true position since they cannot be put under tension by the spools.

The back of the camera, with its positive eyepiece, is then replaced, and the eyepiece adjusted so that the scratches on the surface of the film are seen with maximum clarity. Care must be taken over this operation; it may be helpful to point the open-shuttered camera at a light—stopped down, if necessary, by the iris diaphragm to reduce glare and improve definition. This is the only time we need to use the iris diaphragm: normally it is left wide open, and, preferably, fixed in some manner against accidental movement.

Pre-focusing adjustments, as they may be termed, need not be done at the telescope unless this is found more convenient to the worker. There are several ways of locking an eyepiece in any predetermined position; small grub-screws let into the wall of the ferrule containing the eyepiece will be found adequate, or a locking-ring round a split ferrule working something like a hose-grip, will also lock the eyepiece.

The performance of no two eyes is the same—even the two eyes of the same observer; the same eye should therefore always be used for the pre-focusing as for the subsequent telescope work. Short-sightedness produces greater errors in focusing than long-sightedness. Periodic checking of the eyepiece–emulsion relationship should be carried out.

89

The high-power eyepiece at the back of the camera is kept covered when not in use. The front of the eyepiece is set back slightly from the surrounding level of the wooden back of the camera, and a 'keyhole cover' is easily slid across it to exclude stray light. An eyepiece projecting above the surface would require a screw-on or press-on cap.

So much for the focusing mechanism. The rest of the camera contains the usual features of the 35mm. miniature camera. The photographs and diagrams in this chapter illustrate the details of its construction, and it is hoped that these, together with the text, will enable the reader to construct one on similar lines, if he so desires.

Construction

There are certain essential components common to every 35mm. camera. These are:

(1) A light-tight box forming the body of the camera.
(2) Two film spools. Film travels from one to the other when the winding knobs are turned.
(3) Located between the two spools, what, for the want of a better name, might be termed the 'frame block'.
(4) The film pressure plate.

To these can be added shutters, frame-counting devices, lenses, and so on.

Camera bodies can be made of metal, but from the amateur constructor's point of view wood is more suitable. Sound, well-seasoned and preferably close-grained wood should be used; mahogany and teak are admirable. Mine is of mahogany and is made of six pieces of wood—it looks more like a small cigar-box than a camera. The back and bottom are screwed and glued together making one L-shaped piece which can be completely removed. Screwed to the back is a flanged ferrule of brass containing the positive high-power eyepiece. The 'keyhole cover' is attached to the outer wooden surface of the back. Inside, on two thin strips of phosphor-bronze is the metal pressure plate for the film. A small hole, concentric with the eyepiece, allows the operator to carry out the focusing operation.

Four pieces of wood comprise the front of the box. Two of these are, of course, the opposite numbers of those forming the L-shaped

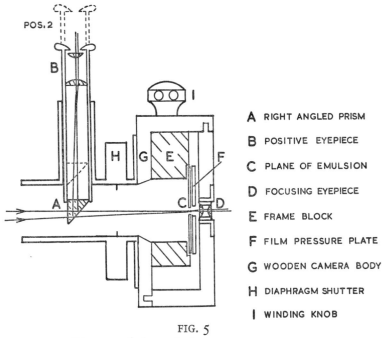

A RIGHT ANGLED PRISM

B POSITIVE EYEPIECE

C PLANE OF EMULSION

D FOCUSING EYEPIECE

E FRAME BLOCK

F FILM PRESSURE PLATE

G WOODEN CAMERA BODY

H DIAPHRAGM SHUTTER

I WINDING KNOB

FIG. 5

Diagram of the author's 35mm. astro-camera

In the first position, the right-angled prism, A, deflects incoming rays into the eyepiece, B. With the object in view the 'prismatic eyepiece' is withdrawn to position 2, and light can then enter the camera. Focusing adjustments are facilitated by the positive eyepiece, D, which is sharply focused on the plane of the emulsion, C. A small hole is punched in the film.

back, and the two shorter pieces are the ends. Thus, the two main components of the camera body consist respectively of two and four pieces. In the interests of light exclusion the edges of these two main sections are tongued-and-grooved, so as to form light-traps.

The front of the wooden box houses the two winding mechanisms, the 'frame block', a film counting device and the shutter. The front of the shutter is adapted so as to fit the draw-tube of the telescope. Care in the drilling of the box is needed to ensure correct alignment of all the optical parts. The axis of the draw-tube must pass centrally through that of the shutter, frame block, pressure plate and focusing eyepiece, in that order.

The frame block is made of metal and is screwed to the wooden case—it could be, equally well, made from hard wood. The frame block supports the film which travels across it emulsion-side downwards; the emulsion would in fact be badly scratched were not provision made for it in the form of wide, shallow grooves. One of these is cut across the block and is rather more than 35mm. wide and a shade deeper than the film thickness. The second is cut centrally within the first, leaving a step either side; these steps support little more than the perforated edges of the film. The emulsion then travels across without damage. All sharp edges are rounded and polished, and a large aperture is cut in the frame block to the width of the second groove. In my own camera, this hole is rectangular, but a round one will do if the reader finds this easier to make. The hole determines the size of the film frame, for light from the telescope and shutter is admitted through it.

The pressure plate on the back of the camera maintains the film in intimate contact with the frame block, thus ensuring that the plane of the emulsion coincides with the image plane.

Most probably the reader will prefer to use ordinary 35mm. spools as supplied by the film manufacturers. Alternatively he could make his own from brass. A small metal-turning lathe is essential for this work but this need not be an elaborate machine; mine is a small treadle lathe of the round-bedded type.

The barrels of the spools are made hollow at one end, so as to allow the slotted winding spindle to be inserted and engage with a brass pin placed diametrically across the inside. As with the commercial spools, the other ends are made to project above the upper flanges. This allows hinged retaining members, with holes rather larger than the spool barrels, to fit loosely over the spools and hold them in place.

Before inserting a spool in the camera, the hinged member is pulled upward, and when the spool is correctly placed with the winding spindle it is released and is pulled by a tight helical spring firmly down on to the upper flange of the spool. There are two of these hinged members—one for each spool—attached by their hinges to either side of the frame block.

The winding spindles rotate in turned, brass-flanged bushes let into the wood of the case. The winding knobs are small bakelite radio knobs with the standard $\frac{1}{4}$-inch hole. Both winding spindles are made $\frac{1}{4}$-inch in diameter to fit the knobs and brass bushes, but on the inside of the camera they are left larger, and fit loosely into the film spools. Thus each spindle has a shoulder moving against the inner surface of the brass bush—the latter is purposely left a little proud of the wood on the inside of the box. A small domed spring washer is placed between the knob and the external end of the bush to provide a little friction in the winding spindle. Without a certain amount of friction there is a tendency for the film to unwind upon the spool like a clockspring. Friction is also supplied by the tight helical spring between the retaining member and the upper flange of the film spool.

To test the proper working of the film wind, one film spool can be loaded with used film and inserted into the camera. The L-shaped back need not be replaced. The end of the film is attached to the take-up spool and winding is started. Winding the film across should neither be too easy nor too stiff; if it is, the winding knobs and the tension on the spring washers must be adjusted. The film must also be nicely aligned with the wider slot in the frame block, as otherwise it will be damaged.

There is no absolute need to include a frame counter in this type of camera, but obviously no reliance can be placed upon the turning of the take-up knob since this is rolling up far more film per turn at the end of operations than at the beginning. Several solutions of this problem suggest themselves. We could, for example, devise a dial geared from the take-up spindle and

93

engraved with a 'folded-up' type of scale in which the frame numbers get progressively closer. Other ideas include 'clickers' giving audible information each time a perforation passes a given point. The length of film could be measured by the number of clicks.

My own counter takes a more orthodox form, and employs two small-toothed wheels meshing with the film perforations. The wheels are fixed to a common spindle, housed in the metal frame block. If counters are to be included, the frame block should be made of metal, for wood (if it gets damp) is likely to 'seize' on the spindle. Alternatively, metal bushes or bearings fitted to the frame block will avoid this trouble.

The spindle is made long enough to project through the wooden top of the camera, projecting from the same face as the winding knobs.

Ideally, the number of teeth on the wheels should permit one complete turn of the spindle per frame. This rotation can be reduced by either a gear train or, in the case of my camera, a worm and wheel driving an equally divided scale numbered from 1 to 20. One complete rotation of this scale against a suitable pointer indicates that twenty frames of film have been used. If the strip of film is long enough, the scale may be allowed to make a second rotation, at the end of which the score will be forty frames. The spools cannot hold much more than this amount of film; five-foot reloads provide but thirty-six exposures in the commercial 35mm. camera, so these can be used without trouble.

In practice, the toothed wheels turned by the film perforations are set in narrow slots in the metal frame block. Not much can be seen of them normally, since the teeth are the only parts which extend above the surfaces of the steps supporting the film. The film pressure plate is slotted in the appropriate places to avoid the teeth which would otherwise rub against it.

The spindle bearing the toothed wheels is capped by a flat disc of brass. Soldered to this on the upper surface is a cut-out arrow of the same material. The passage of one frame of film imparts one complete rotation to the embossed arrow. This is useful in the

94

dark, for it is possible to feel the rotation instead of seeing it; in my opinion it is more valuable than the actual counter. On the other hand, having made the toothed wheels and fitted the spindle, it is not a difficult job to finish the complete counting device. Meccano spindles, worms and wheels can be put to good use here.

This camera, obviously, must be loaded and unloaded in the dark, and must therefore be simple to deal with. Much thought was given to this point when designing it. The fact that the wooden back of the camera really consists of two sides is in itself an advantage. The removal of the back and one side allows the operator to get his fingers inside the camera, and this facilitates loading. The hinged retaining members for the spools are also simple to use. Another cut-out arrow of thin aluminium screwed to the wood adjacent to the take-up knob, not only indicates the direction it must turn—but also tells the photographer which *is* the take-up knob. Simple, but nevertheless very useful in the dark.

The two wooden parts of the camera must be efficiently held together. Wide, strong elastic bands have been used successfully, but more permanent fittings are desirable. Those employed in my camera are easier to draw than to describe, and are well seen in the photographs. Hinged at either end of the main body of the camera is a piece of small-diameter threaded rod. A terminal head, threaded internally to suit the rod, screws on to it. At the other end, the rod hinges on a steel pin linking it to a small brass fitting screwed to the wooden ends of the camera. The other portion is made from one piece of brass about $\frac{1}{8}$-inch thick; if it is thinner than this it might cause trouble by bending. At one end the brass is drilled to accommodate the threaded rod. The top of this hole is slightly recessed to receive the terminal head; this makes doubly sure that the head cannot move outward from the camera once it has been tightened. Of course this cannot happen until the hole has been slotted with two hacksaw cuts, the central short piece of brass between the hole and the end of the fitting being removed. The resultant slot must be smoothed with a thin flat file until the threaded rod can slide easily into it from the end. Fixing holes for woodscrews complete this part.

The operation of these two fittings is simple, and easy to manage in the dark. First, the two portions of the camera are put together, the hinged rods with terminal heads being swung out of the way. When the two halves of the camera are accurately located, the hinged members are swung towards the back of the camera and inserted into the slots provided in the $\frac{1}{8}$-inch brass; once they are in their recessed holes the terminal heads are screwed down. This holds the two camera parts firmly together. Blobs of solder applied to the ends of the threaded rods prevent the terminal heads from coming completely unscrewed in the Stygian darkness that accompanies film loading.

So much for the body of the camera, the frame block, winding mechanisms, counters and focusing eyepiece. One important item must still be added before an exposure can be attempted: the shutter.

Focal plane shutters are integral parts of camera bodies and cannot be used with this particular design. We must choose between the metal-leaved diaphragm type and the cardboard flap-type shutter. If the latter is used, some provision must be made for protecting the unexposed film in the camera. Clearly, the loaded camera cannot be transported to and from the telescope without some means of preventing light from entering the very substantial aperture at the front. It might conceivably be placed in a light-tight box or wrapped in thick black cloth, but these are only makeshifts and, sooner or later, the inevitable will happen, accompanied by much vexation. My camera is fitted with a flat metal slide which can be used to mask the unexposed film whenever necessary. This works in grooves within the frame-block, its action being similar to that of the protective cover on a plate-holder. It can be removed and replaced by a similar piece of metal with an aperture cut in it —a welcome addition when photographing Venus in daylight. It is not always within the skill and experience of the operator to gauge his exposures so that the planet is recorded without the film being fogged by the light sky. The normal frame is a good deal too large for planetary work and the aperture in the flat metal slide allows plenty of image space without wasting too much emulsion on the surrounding sky. In this way about three images per frame can be secured. When photographing the planets at night there is no need to use this gadget, since the dark sky does not record on the emulsion.

Whether or not this useful appendage will be included must rest with the individual; but some method of reducing the effective size of the frame must be incorporated. The stop must be fairly close to the film—the distance between them should not exceed about three-quarters of an inch.

Excellent results can be achieved with this type of metal slide in conjunction with the flap-type shutter on the upper end of the telescope.

The metal-leaved diaphragm-type of shutter is doubtless the safest choice for our astronomical camera. It can be fitted to the front of the camera by whatever means are dictated by its construction. The shutter is mounted on a commercial camera by a projecting tube, which is normally screw-cut on the outside and is fitted with a large retaining ring or nut which can be tightened upon it. The hole in the wooden front of the astronomical camera can be enlarged to accept this retaining ring, and a thin metal plate fitted over the entire front of the camera. A hole, just large enough to take the screw-cut tube of the shutter, and concentric with the hole in the camera front, must be made in the metal plate. The shutter tube is then pushed through the hole in the metal plate and the retaining ring tightened on the back, making the shutter immovable. The plate and shutter are held to the camera-front with wood-screws.

An alternative method, which can be employed if the retaining ring is of brass, is to solder the ring to the front of the metal plate. This saves the job of enlarging the hole in the wood. Care must be taken to see that the shutter tightens to the correct position; in other words, the name on the shutter must be correctly orientated with the camera body. Corrections can be made with shims or thin metal washers placed between shutter and retaining ring.

97

G

If the retaining ring has a wide enough flange, it will be possible to drill and screw it to the wooden front direct. This is to be recommended when the ring is of aluminium or one of its alloys, which are tricky to solder effectively; the lower melting point aluminium solder tends to be rather unsatisfactory, while the higher melting point ones often flow at a temperature too near the melting point of the job itself.

Failing all else a brass ring, screw-cut to fit the tube or barrel of the shutter, can be made on a lathe.

The shutter aperture must not be too small. For the standard $1\frac{1}{4}$-inch tube, it would be unwise to use an aperture much less than 1-inch in diameter. Small shutter apertures may make it difficult to secure uniform light distribution over the whole frame; the resulting 'vignetting' is a nuisance in lunar work.

Adaptor Tubes

Before photographs can be taken, the camera must be fitted firmly to the draw-tube of the telescope in such a way that it can be easily, but not accidentally, removed. Some sort of adaptor is required, and its form will depend on the particular eyepiece fitting used on the telescope. Fixing an adaptor-tube to the front of the camera shutter may involve some screwcutting on a lathe, unless the original lens fitting is available; if it is, it may be possible to solder it to the stock size $1\frac{1}{4}$-inch brass tube. The camera lens cell or fitting—minus the lens—screws into the shutter in the normal way and the projecting adaptor tube fits into the draw-tube of the telescope.

When one tube has to have a tightish sliding fit within another, the usual practice is to slit one of them. Draw-tubes are generally left unslit, so that the tube of the adaptor must be slitted. In the absence of a motorized slitting saw, the job can be done with a 'junior'-type hacksaw. A slit is made in the end of the adaptor tube further from the camera, parallel to the axis of the tube and about an inch long, and its edges are cleaned up. If this does not impart sufficient springiness, another slit is cut at right angles to it at the end nearer to the camera. This cut is continued almost half-way through the tube, equally on each side of the first slit. This produces two springy leaves of brass which can be prised open with a knife blade if the adaptor is still too loose in the draw-tube.

Adaptor tubes should not be more than about 1/16 inch thick. If thinner tubing is used, great care must be exercised in the slitting operations: a hacksaw blade which jams during such work is hampered by the 'pawl and ratchet' effect which results from the fact that the thickness of the tube is less than the distance between adjacent teeth. This trouble can be reduced by cutting the tube at an oblique angle—the saw-blade is then deluded into thinking the wall thicker than it is.

Stray Light

The greatest enemy of photographers is stray light, which always manages to creep in where it is least expected. Every precaution must be taken to eliminate it. The inside of the camera should be dyed black, and all metal parts that do not come in contact with the film painted. Its favourite haunt is the region of the draw-tube and adaptor. Metal surfaces with a rough finish appear shiny when held at grazing angles to the light, and painting them with matt-black paint is of little use by itself. The surface itself must be corrugated in some way. One very effective dodge is to have the inside of the tube screw-cut with a sharp but not too coarse thread—about thirty threads per inch. (A very coarse thread might cut through the tube itself.) Each of these threads acts like a tiny diaphragm.

Black velvet has been a firm favourite for many years but has one serious disadvantage—it will pick up and shed dust, and sooner or later this will find its way on to the film.

Reasonably coarse brass or copper gauze folded to a snug fit in the tube helps to break up reflections, and there are no pieces to come unstuck. Gauze is difficult to paint, but both brass and copper can be blackened chemically.

CAMERAS AND ACCESSORIES

Fixed Diaphragms

Fixed diaphragms of the conventional type can also be fitted in the draw-tube—and, indeed, almost anywhere within the 'small end' providing they do not restrict the aperture of the telescope. They are easily made from short lengths of brass tube and must have at least one true end. The 'trueing up' is most easily done on a lathe, but it can also be done by hand with a file and a set-square, since utmost precision is unnecessary. The flat washer-like diaphragm is cut from a thin brass sheet and is soldered to the true end of the tube. Soldering is not difficult providing the metal is clean. All traces of grease must be removed with some solvent such as petrol, the surfaces having first been cleaned with carborundum or emery paper.

The soldering is accomplished without an iron and may be done over a gas-ring, bunsen burner or spirit lamp, whichever is convenient. A flat piece of metal not less than $\frac{1}{8}$-inch thick is supported over the flame—its size is not important as long as it is larger than the flat piece of brass from which the diaphragm is to be made; this in turn should be only slightly larger than the end of the tube to which it is going to be soldered.

The piece of brass sheet is laid on the metal plate over the flame, and the brass tube stood on it, tube end down. If the tube is not in contact with the brass sheet all the way round, a weight can be placed on the tube. Soldering flux is applied to facilitate the flow of solder at the junction of the two pieces. Heating must not be too violent. When the work is approaching the correct temperature the flux will fizzle and splutter; heating is continued until exploratory moves with a thin piece of solder show that it is able to melt and run round the joint. When the soldering is completed, the job is allowed to cool in its own time; only when the solder has lost its 'quick-silver' appearance is it safe to quench the job under a tap.

All that now remains to be done is to trim away the parts of the metal sheet not required, and to make the central hole in the diaphragm. The outer pieces can be removed carefully with metal shears, so as not to break or prise away the newly-deposited solder. Ideally, the trimming of the outside and the making of the central aperture should be done on a lathe. Failing this the diaphragm can be filed in a small vice; the movement of the file must be in the direction that tends to push the brass sheet against the tube. When the outside is down to size the circular aperture is made. First a circle is scribed on it, concentric with the tube. All within this circle must be removed. One method is to drill a ring of small holes just within the scribed circle and to join these up with a small file. The aperture so obtained can then be made circular with a half-round file and the burrs and rough edges cleaned up. If necessary the tube can be slit, as already described, to ensure a good fit in the draw-tube or wherever it is designed to go.

In placing the diaphragms it is not sufficient to consider axial rays only—if the marginal rays are occluded the performance of the telescope will be impaired. To be on the safe side, the eye, when placed behind the frame aperture, should be able to see the whole of the mirror from any position in the frame.

The camera is now complete. We can load it with film, mount it on the telescope draw-tube, and get on with our first attempts at astronomical photography. But before doing so it will be worthwhile to consider some miscellaneous snags that may be encountered.

Snags

Suppose we wish to attempt lunar photography at the Newtonian focus. This is a modest enough ambition, but even so we may run into difficulties, depending upon the construction of the telescope and the accessibility of the focal plane. Ordinary positive eyepieces pushed into the draw-tube have no difficulty in focusing the focal plane image, as indeed they do whenever they present a sharply focused view to the observer. The camera, however, cannot be placed within the draw-tube like the eyepiece, but is some distance back from it—the distance being equal to the combined depth of shutter and camera. It may therefore be impossible to rack the draw-tube far enough in to bring the emulsion into coincidence with the focal plane. What can be done in this case? The obvious suggestion is to use a shorter draw-tube.

Special interchangeable fittings can be constructed by the better equipped amateur—I have used water pipe fittings and screw-threads quite successfully. The use of standard threads allows all sorts of adaptors to be made for different purposes, and obviates the lengthy and sometimes tedious job of cutting fairly large threads on a lathe. Alternatively, the telescope tube itself can be shortened—just recently I reduced mine by $1\frac{1}{4}$ inches for this very reason—though it is obviously easier to shorten a draw-tube than a telescope tube.

In the Newtonian telescope the secondary reflecting surface may be either a diagonal or a totally reflecting prism. Each has certain advantages and disadvantages. The diagonal is coated with silver or aluminium which has to be renewed occasionally, while the prism requires no such periodic overhauls. The main sources of light loss in a prism are absorption in the glass and the usual air-glass reflections; the latter can be reduced by 'blooming'. My 6-inch telescope was fitted with a totally reflecting prism until I embarked on a programme of ultra-violet photography of Venus in 1956. Since glass absorbs the ultra-violet wavelengths heavily I decided to replace the prism by an aluminized diagonal.

As would be expected from such an exchange the focal plane was moved in closer to the telescope. The prism, ignoring the reflection from the inclined face, behaves like a solid cube of glass. Converging beams of light impinging upon the first plane face are bent towards the normal—that is, tending to parallelism. The opposite effect occurs at the second plane face and the original angles are restored—but by then they are nearer to the eyepiece. With ordinary glasses of refractive index $1\cdot5$, or thereabouts, the image plane is pushed back one third of the effective thickness of the glass.

The Barlow Lens

If we are unable to push the camera far enough in to bring the film to the focal plane, we must pull the latter out towards the

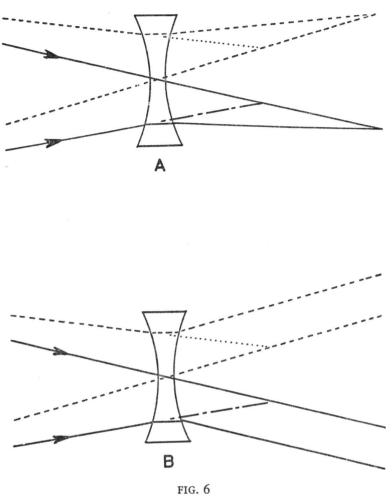

FIG. 6

The Barlow Lens

Placed a short distance inside the focal plane, a Barlow, or negative lens, will increase the effective focal length of the telescope, with a proportional increase in image size. This is shown at A. At B, its distance inside the focal plane has been increased until it is equal to the focal length of the Barlow lens itself: converging cones of rays are then rendered parallel. At this setting it can be used as a Galilean eyepiece.

camera. In other words, the effective focal length of the telescope must be slightly increased. To do this we enlist the help of an old astronomical friend—the Barlow lens, which, in its simplest form is a simple bi-concave (*i.e.*, negative) lens. Unlike a magnifying glass, it has no 'real' focal plane, so that it cannot itself produce focused images on a screen.

Being a negative lens it tends to 'open out' the light rays passing through it. Parallel rays become divergent; a converging cone tends towards parallelism, while diverging beams are rendered even more so. The amount the convergence or divergence of a cone is altered is greatly influenced by the position at which the Barlow intercepts it.

As an example, let us consider the effect of a Barlow lens on the cone of rays converging from a telescope mirror. Suppose that the negative focal length of the Barlow is 3 inches, which is a reasonable value. But before going on, some clarification of this point may be needed. We have already seen the Barlow cannot form real images, but only virtual images. It is therefore not easy to measure the focal length of a negative lens directly. A parallel beam of rays entering the lens axially is made to diverge. If these diverging rays are projected back through the lens to their point of intersection on its axis, the distance of this point from the centre of the lens is its (negative) focal length. From the practical viewpoint, a 3-inch focal length negative lens will cancel the magnifying effect of a 3-inch focal length positive lens, so that their combined performance will be the same as that of a piece of plane glass.

The converging cone of rays from the telescope mirror will, if allowed, come to a focus and produce an image in the mirror's focal plane. But if a Barlow lens is inserted into the cone just in front of the focal plane, its action in reducing the convergence of the rays will cause them to come to a focus behind the original focal plane (*i.e.*, further from the mirror).

This is how the Barlow lens can be useful to us, for by increasing the mirror's effective focal length, the images are brought to a focus further from the telescope tube, where we can arrange for them to fall on the emulsion in the camera. Slightly larger images coupled with some absorption of light in the lens will necessitate rather longer exposures when the Barlow is used.

If we continue to push the lens forward into the cone of rays the focal length will increase steadily, till the focal plane is well beyond the limits of any practicable draw-tube. The limit is reached when the 3-inch focal length Barlow is 3 inches inside the focal plane of the mirror: the converging cone will then be transmitted by the lens as a parallel beam. Any advance of the lens past the 3-inch mark will produce a diverging cone of completely useless rays.

It is important to understand the action of the Barlow lens, because descriptions of it have often been over-simplified. In the above account we simply considered a cone of rays converging to a single star image situated upon the optical axis; but we must not ignore what happens to off-axial rays of light. Off-axial rays are collected from stars lying near the edge of the field of the telescope. Their parallel rays thus enter the instrument at an angle to its axis—and after reflection at the primary mirror and the flat come to a focus near the side of the field.

If the 3-inch focal length Barlow lens is made to intercept them three inches in front of the focal plane, the converging cones of starlight are transformed into parallel beams. Axial rays continue along the optical axis of the mirror-lens combination. The off-axial rays from a given star also emerge as a parallel beam; but although the rays forming this beam are parallel to one another, the different beams themselves diverge. Thus the further back we go from the lens, the more widely separated will be the individual star images, although each of them is composed of parallel rays and remains the same size at all distances from the lens.

The principles involved in the above discussion are by no means new, and were known to Galileo who was making his own telescopes as long ago as 1609. He did not use mirrors for his objectives, but he did employ negative eyelenses arranged to deliver substantially parallel bundles of rays into the eye. One of the disadvantages of the Galilean telescope is that the size of the field of view varies with the position of the observer's eye. A larger field will be seen if his eye is placed nearly in contact with the back surface of the negative eyelens than when his eye is some distance back from the lens, when it can admit only the more central rays. Only by moving his eye from the centre can he make the edges of the field come into view.

Commercial cameras can be used in conjunction with telescopes using negative eyepieces by employing the same tactics that were adopted with the more conventional positive eyepiece. The camera lens should be as large as possible, so as to accept as many of the marginal rays as possible, and for the same reason it should be placed close to the negative eyepiece; otherwise the field will be very restricted. The camera lens must of course be set at infinity.

Simple negative lenses give less satisfactory results than achromats, since they decompose the marginal rays into short spectra and thus give inferior definition at the edges of the field. The axial rays are least affected.

One advantage with the negative eyepiece is the greater amount of light which can enter the camera. Instead of the separated lenses of a positive eyepiece, with four air-glass or glass-air surfaces, we have a cemented combination whose two external surfaces may be 'bloomed' to reduce losses by reflection even further. Huyghenian eyepieces, although also known as negative eyepieces, are not suitable for photographic work.

It is worth emphasizing that the only difference between a short focus Barlow lens and a negative Galilean ocular is the manner of their use—if the lens is used to increase the effective focal length of the objective it is a Barlow, but when placed so as to transmit parallel light from the telescope it takes on the role of an ocular.

Finding the Focal Length of a Negative Lens

A simple and practical way of measuring the focal length of a negative lens is worth knowing. Parallel light from the Sun is allowed to fall axially upon the lens. The diverging rays transmitted by the lens are intercepted by a sheet of white card, on which they illuminate an area that is larger than the lens. The

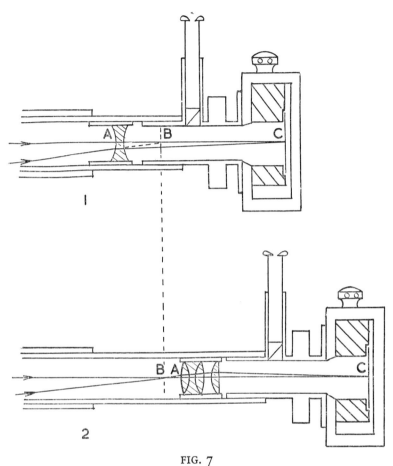

FIG. 7

Enlarging telescopic images for the camera

In both instances A is the enlarging lens, B the Newtonian focal plane of the telescope, and C the plane of the film emulsion.

In 1, a Barlow or negative lens inside the focal plane intercepts the converging light rays, resulting in a shorter draw-tube than in 2 where the positive eyepiece intercepts diverging rays outside the Newtonian focus.

distance between lens and card is varied until the circle of light upon the card is twice the diameter of the lens: this distance is the (negative) focal length. To facilitate the procedure, a circle whose diameter is twice the *clear* aperture of the lens should be drawn on the card.

Negative v. Positive Magnification of Telescopic Images

For the most part, images of the planets in the Newtonian focus are too small to be photographed; so are the ones given by the mirror-Barlow combination, unless the latter is very strong (*i.e.*, short focal length). Large images from ordinary Barlow lenses are formed too far from the draw-tube of the telescope to be used conveniently. We could, of course, devise a 'trombone'-type telescope folding the light back on itself a few times, but this would only achieve what a positive eyepiece can do with a lot less trouble. High-power good-quality eyepieces, placed within the draw-tube, will project highly-magnified images of the planets into the camera. There is only one snag here—most eyepieces have some sort of metal flange which prevents them from being pushed completely into the telescope draw-tube. The way this difficulty is overcome must rest with the reader, who must choose between the mutilation of the eyepiece fitting and the making of a new one.

Restricted Fields

When the eyepiece has been fitted in the draw-tube, the camera, on its adaptor, can also be plugged into the end of it; enough space must be left between the end of the draw-tube and the eyepiece to allow for this. We are now equipped to photograph the planets or small areas of the Moon, using high magnification and a restricted field of view. Restricting the field raises another problem: for how are we to be sure the object we wish to photograph is within the field of the camera? The initial focusing, with the positive eyepiece at the back of the camera, will show the object in the correct place to start with; but the telescope may be

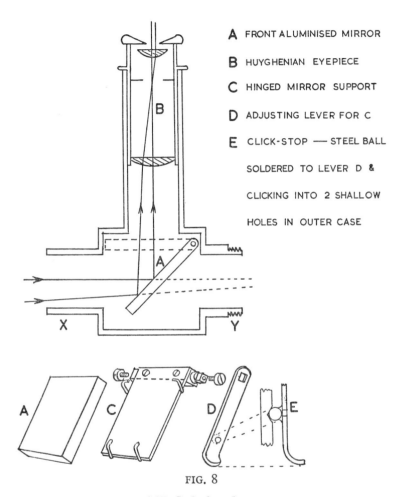

A FRONT ALUMINISED MIRROR

B HUYGHENIAN EYEPIECE

C HINGED MIRROR SUPPORT

D ADJUSTING LEVER FOR C

E CLICK-STOP — STEEL BALL
SOLDERED TO LEVER D &
CLICKING INTO 2 SHALLOW
HOLES IN OUTER CASE

FIG. 8

A 'Reflex' Attachment

This plugs into the draw-tube at X, *and screws on to the diaphragm-type camera shutter at* Y. A, *the mirror, is held to the hinged support,* C, *by* 18 *SWG copper wire claws soldered to the underside. The adjusting lever,* D, *on the outside of the reflex housing, is easily operated to remove the mirror before an exposure.*

knocked out of alignment, or there may be some drift in the mechanical drive.

We have already touched upon the subject of long-focus guiding telescopes, mounted on the tube of the main instrument. High power eyepieces used in conjunction with thickish cross-wires should enable us to keep the chosen object within the field of the camera. Routine checking of both telescopes for alignment should always be carried out prior to starting photographic work.

Undoubtedly the most satisfactory way of finding the where-abouts of the image of the chosen object is to look into the draw-tube itself. If we cut a hole in the side of the camera adaptor tube, just in front of the shutter, we could place a small mirror or prism to intercept the incoming rays and deflect them through the newly-cut hole so that we could examine them.

This, in essence, is what the 'prismatic eyepiece' on my astro-camera (Fig. 5) consists of. The construction of this is not too complicated and its advantages more than outweigh the trouble of making it.

The Prismatic Eyepiece

A tube, smaller than the adaptor tube in diameter, is fixed to form a right-angle with the adaptor tube. Within the first tube slides a second, containing a small prism at the lower end, and an eyepiece at the top. The eyepiece need not be of high quality—mine was made from two odd small lenses. Its purpose is not to define, but simply to show if the object is within the field of the camera or not. In the first, or working position, the sliding inner tube containing prism and eyepiece is lowered, periscope-wise, till the prism intercepts the central rays in the adaptor tube. The axis of these is turned through 90° into the eyepiece. Position (2) is used when the observer has satisfied himself that the object is, in fact, the one he wants, and pulls the tube upwards out of the path of the incoming light. Click stops ensure positive settings of the prismatic eyepiece.

The field of this device is admittedly small, as I found when using Dr. W. H. Steavenson's 30-inch reflector for photography. Quite often the object was known to be close to the very restricted field of the prismatic eyepiece, but for all that, it was sometimes rather elusive. Perhaps this is not so surprising when we remember that the effective focal length of the combined optical elements was of the order of 100 feet, and the field no more than a few seconds of arc across.

A larger field will result if, instead of intercepting only central rays, we use all of them. The traditional reflex mirror does this. This is a front-surfaced mirror which fulfils the same function as that of our prism, and has two positions corresponding to those of the prism. Instead of being withdrawn to position (2) it hinges from one end. Click stops ensure accurate and permanent alignment.

To make full use of the reflex mirror a low power eyepiece is desirable. Low powers, however, have greater focal lengths and need longer tubes to accommodate them. The overall result, using positive eyepieces, would be clumsy and perhaps weighty. With this in mind I turned my attention to the Huyghenian eyepiece which, unlike positive eyepieces, has an internal focal plane; this allows the eyepiece to be placed nearer to the focal plane of the objective than a positive eyepiece and provides low powers without undue prolongation of supporting tubes.

Loading the Camera

Loading the camera with film is an important part of the proceedings. Most commercial cameras are designed to take loaded cassettes containing enough film for 36 normal-sized frames. Cassettes are not used in the author's camera—all too often they turn out to be 'scratchettes', particularly those employing velvet light-traps.

Film may be purchased in bulk or in the five-foot reload lengths. The spool to be loaded should be removed from the camera and one end of the film attached to it. There are all sorts of ways of achieving this, depending upon the type of spool and its fitting.

The specially constructed spools in my camera have slots through which the ends of the film are inserted and clamped by a locking device.

Elaborate spools like these are not essential, and film can be attached to the barrel of any spool quite simply with adhesive tape. Slotted barrels without locking devices allow film to be inserted and project from the opposite side, where the next overlaying turn of film binds it to the spool. Cutting the film ends V-shaped sometimes helps where slots are involved.

Efficient locking arrangements are useful where film has to be reeled backwards and forwards in the camera and there is danger of pulling it out of one of the spools.

Spools can be hand-fed with film—a tedious and uncertain process—or a simple mechanical winder can be bought or contrived which will enable film to be wound easily, quickly and safely. I bought mine at a camera shop 'bargain' sale. It comprises, basically, a U-shaped frame supporting a small handle turning a slotted winding spindle. The film spool fixed within the frame is driven by the slotted member and a spring-loaded piston-like member at the opposite end supplies enough pressure to maintain the spool in place. A flat metal leaf bears upon the film, feeding it accurately on to the barrel of the spool. No doubt a suitable winder could rapidly be made from Meccano parts.

Care must be taken when attaching the film to the spool, so that it has no tendency to ride up over the flanges due to lateral displacement. The parent roll from which the spool is loaded should also be guarded against sideways movement of adjacent turns which, if permitted, will scratch and damage the emulsion. Most people are familiar with this effect which allows an otherwise flat roll of film to be transformed miraculously into a long 'magic wand'. If the parent roll is wound on a spool or bobbin this cannot occur.

When loading a camera in total darkness, the operator must know the whereabouts of all the various pieces of equipment. Nothing is more conducive to bad language than losing a vital item just when it is needed. Loading is best done on a large flat surface

—a table-top will do—and all the paraphernalia should be kept well away from the edges. Tools such as scissors and punches must also be placed conveniently. Dress rehearsals with used film help in no small way to familiarize the worker with the loading operations.

Before replacing the back of a newly-loaded camera which employs a focusing eyepiece, we must not forget to punch a small hole through the film. Possibly a punch may be regarded as a luxury, for the hole in the film could be cut almost as well with pointed scissors, but the punch is easier and quicker to use and the hole is always well placed. The hole should not be less than about 5mm., or three-sixteenths of an inch in diameter. The punch is made from an old pair of pliers—a 5mm. protruding flat-ended pin fitted to one jaw enters a suitable hole in the opposite one when the jaws are brought together. The distance from the centre of the protruding pin to the bottom of the jaws is half the width of the film—17·5mm.

With film stretching from one spool to the other, it is only necessary to advance the loaded spool a small amount to produce a loop of slack film. It is an easy matter to open the punch and insert the edge of the film as far into the jaws as it will go. The punch is then operated like the conventional railway ticket punch and the perforation appears, just where it is needed, in the centre of the film. The slack film is taken up again and the newly made perforation placed centrally with the camera aperture. Further adjustments can be made with the winding knobs after the camera has been sealed against the light.

Film must always be handled carefully by the edges. On no account must the surface of the emulsion come in contact with the operator's fingers—even if they *are* clean. Before turning on the light, make sure that the positive eyepiece is covered, that the shutter is closed, and the camera back securely fixed.

CHAPTER 5

Photographing the Moon

The Moon, situated less than a quarter of a million miles away from us, is a glorious object in the telescope and a fascinating world to photograph. Its surface, never obscured by clouds and atmosphere, presents a beautiful but pitiless landscape of flat plains, mountain masses, and craters of unequalled grandeur.

It is advisable that we should use the Moon for our initial experiments: we shall learn much to help us in later and less parochial photographic work, and until we can obtain satisfactory pictures of the Moon there is little point in sacrificing film on more distant members of the Solar System.

Several factors have to be considered before we can press the shutter release and secure our first lunar pictures. These fall into two separate groups—the factors we cannot control and the ones we can. Within certain limits the former indicate the latter. First are the independent factors:

(1) Atmospheric conditions.

(2) Moon's altitude above observer's horizon.

(3) Moon's phases.

(4) Moon's distance from Earth.

These four largely determine the following:

(5) Size of Moon's image upon a given emulsion, sub-divided into:

  (*a*) Prime focal images.

  (*b*) Enlarged images of whole surface.

  (*c*) Greatly enlarged images of selected portions.

(6) Film speed.

(7) Length of exposure.

Coupled with these, is the unknown efficiency of the telescope's reflecting surfaces and the losses by absorption in the lenses, etc. Let us consider all these factors in turn.

(1) Atmospheric conditions

Exposures of more than a few seconds are undesirable for two main reasons. In the first place, it is not a simple matter to keep the telescope accurately aligned on moving objects for prolonged periods. Secondly, turbulence in the Earth's atmosphere, unless conditions are unusually good, keeps the images in a confused and boiling state. It is impossible to anticipate moments of good 'seeing'.

As well as natural atmospheric turbulence there is the manmade variety caused by currents of warm air from chimneys and the like. In addition, after hot sunny days, rooftops and buildings return part of their heat to the surrounding air. Warm air refracts light less than the cold mixed with it; it is through this evermoving mixture that the astronomer has, all too often, to make his observations.

Photography suffers to a greater extent than visual observation, because the observer's eye is able to benefit from extremely brief moments of good 'seeing'. Film emulsions cannot differentiate good from bad 'seeing' and record everything impartially. For this reason, short exposures stand improved chances of 'stopping' the turbulence and therefore of capturing finer detail.

Guiding upon craters for long exposures often leads to disappointment. It is useless to attempt it with 'gossamer'-type mountings—no vibration can be tolerated, and even with good solid mountings no good will come of it if 'seeing' conditions are poor. Bad 'seeing' causes every point of the image to describe varying circles round its average position—multiply this effect and some idea of the fuzzy results may be imagined.

Turbulence from localized sources is best avoided by setting up the telescope as far from them as circumstances permit. As a general rule, it is desirable that the telescope should command an unobstructed view of the heavens to the south (for an observer in the northern hemisphere).

This brings us to factor (2), since celestial bodies attain their greatest altitude when they are due south. Also there is then less absorption of their light in the atmosphere and the effect of refraction is reduced. At low altitudes, the light from a body travels through a considerable thickness of atmosphere and is dispersed into a short spectrum—in the inverting telescope the red images are above the blue ones. The resultant loss of detail can sometimes be reduced by balancing the non-achromatism of an eyepiece against the effects of atmospheric dispersion.

At its September 1956 opposition, Mars was low in the sky for northern observers, being some 10° south of the celestial equator. It was thus heavily affected by atmospheric refraction and dispersion. Mr. H. E. Dall, of Luton, obtained excellent photographs of the planet using a special optical fitting of his own manufacture, which compensated the dispersion and restored finer detail.

The 'seeing' should always be carefully studied before photography is attempted. If stars at the zenith are seen to be twinkling there is not much point in carrying on. Scudding cloud masses are sometimes harbingers of bad 'seeing' in the clear spaces between them. Excellent 'seeing' often accompanies slight haze, whereas ever-thickening haze—the forerunner of rainy weather—should tell the astronomical photographer to close down and do something else. In the British Isles, cold air-streams from the east nearly always lead to poor 'seeing'. Calm weather coming closely on the heels of prolonged rain, often brings good observing conditions with it.

These are only tendencies. There is no way of predicting good conditions and weather forecasters are not always reliable.

(3) The Lunar Phases

The lunar phases are a constant source of interest to the amateur. To the photographer, however, they are of even greater concern, for to a large extent they control the exposures he must give to record them. More complications arise than appear at first sight. The Moon's surface is by no means smooth, neither does light reflect equally from every part of it; the maria, for example, are noticeably darker than the mountainous regions. The late H. H. Waters[1] quoted figures suggesting that the full Moon is 8·7 times as bright as the first quarter, and 10 times as bright as the last. The eastern regions are darker than the western, since they include Mare Imbrium and Mare Nubium as well as the Oceanus Procellarum.

This does not mean that our exposures should be multiplied by these factors, for we are comparing one area with another twice as large. We can therefore assume an average half of the full Moon to be $4\frac{1}{2}$ times as bright as the first quarter and 5 times as brilliant as the last quarter.

The late Prof. E. S. King[2] said of the Moon, 'At the quarter the total light is reduced to about one-eighth.' This hints at a factor of four, which is supported by Sidgwick.[3] He, starting with a factor of 1 for the full Moon, suggests 4 for both quarters and 12 for crescents aged $3\frac{1}{2}$ days and $24\frac{1}{2}$ days. The amateur, trying to reconcile these factors with shutter speeds, will have to compromise. If 1/10 second is adequate for the full Moon, the other phases will have to be given $\frac{1}{2}$ and 1 second respectively.

The region of the Moon's terminator (the dividing line between the dark and the sunlit halves of the disc) poses its own problems. Assuming that the exposure is correctly gauged for the brightly-illuminated part, then the terminator region will be underexposed. If the latter is correctly exposed, the former will be overexposed. In practice we tend to ignore the terminator and expose for the brighter areas; this results in lunar images exhibiting false ages.

My own experiments indicate that exposures should be increased by a factor of 2 or 3 for the terminator regions. False age

[1] Waters, H. H. *Astronomical Photography.* 1921.
[2] King, E. S. *A Manual of Celestial Photography.* 1931.
[3] Sidgwick, J. B. *Observational Astronomy for Amateurs.* 1954.

effects can be corrected with special shutters, but usually the amateur is prepared to put up with them.

Favourable apparitions of the Moon at different phases

The altitude of the Moon, at each phase, varies continuously throughout the year, and since both visual and photographic observation is most favourably undertaken when the object observed is as far as possible above the horizon, this is an important point to remember. The following table shows when each lunar phase can be observed under the most favourable conditions of altitude, and whereabouts in the sky it is then situated. (Southern observers must add six months and substitute N for S.)

Waxing Crescent	April	S.W. after sunset.
First Quarter	March	S.W. after sunset.
Full Moon	December–January	S. at midnight.
Third Quarter	September	S.E. before sunrise.
Waning Crescent	July	S.E. before sunrise.

(4) The Moon's distance from Earth

By virtue of its non-circular orbit around us, the Moon's distance and therefore its apparent size vary within definite limits.

At perigee, its closest, the angular diameter exceeds $33\frac{1}{2}$ minutes of arc. This drops to approximately $29\frac{1}{2}$ minutes of arc at apogee. The diameter of the lunar image on the negative may therefore vary at different times in the ratio of 8:7—not a negligible variation. We can select the favourable apparitions from the *Nautical Almanac* or the *Handbook of the British Astronomical Association*. Theoretically, we should be able to record finer detail when the Moon is at perigee.

Changes in the Moon's distance cause its brightness to vary in the ratio of 4:3. Waters[1] advocated one-fourth shorter and one-third longer exposures in compensation, but I doubt whether we

[1] Waters, H. H. *Astronomical Photography*. 1921.

118

could, in practice, provide the required shutter speeds. Suppose we were using a shutter-speed of $\frac{1}{2}$ second and wish to increase it by one-third; the increased exposure would therefore be 2/3 second, and this is still nearer $\frac{1}{2}$ than 1 second—the latter being the next slower speed with the majority of shutters. So we remain at $\frac{1}{2}$ second. In any case most emulsions have enough latitude to allow for such errors, and owners of small telescopes can disregard variations in light intensity arising from variations of the Moon's distance.

Other factors can be more serious. Small amounts of haze, for example, may cause appreciable absorption of the actinic short-wave end of the spectrum although they are barely discernible with the naked eye. Variations in emulsions and developers, temperature, and agitation all introduce bigger variables than that due to differences in the Moon's distance.

So much for the uncontrollable factors.

(5) The Moon's image size

With a 6-inch mirror of 49-inch focal length, like the one I use, we obtain a focal image of the Moon rather less than half an inch in diameter. So small an image affects the photographic emulsion quickly, so that we can employ slower and more contrasty and finer-grained emulsions. It would, indeed, be nonsensical to use faster films in such work, for their greater graininess would cause much of the finer detail to be lost.

It is a general rule that we must always use the slowest emulsion that can give a good negative with a short exposure. In all our work we must strive to discover the optimum balance between emulsion speed and exposure.

Small lunar images can be completely spoilt by tiny blemishes and dust particles. On the other hand, being small they have a greater chance of missing such defects in the emulsion completely. No matter how meticulously clean and methodical the worker may be there is no completely effective safeguard against this hazard. Every precaution should be taken to combat the menace of the 'dust bug'. Even so, we can never be really rid of him, but if he is seen to be sleeping innocuously, the rule to follow is 'do not disturb'.

Lunar images in the focal plane of the objective contain extremely fine detail which is lost in emulsion diffusion. At the prime focus of an $f/8$ telescope the linear diameter of an Airy disc (given perfect atmospheric conditions) will be one-third of a thousandth of an inch ($1/120$mm.); the smallest element of detail resolvable in the telescope will be less than this—something like one-sixth of a thousandth of an inch across. To show detail of this size, an emulsion would have to be capable of resolving over 6,000 lines per inch, or about 240 lines per millimetre, which in itself would be no mean feat for any emulsion of moderate speed. We are therefore compelled to use emulsions of lower resolution, and 1,500 lines per inch or about 60 lines per millimetre are in practice more realistic working figures.

On this basis we can easily compute the minimum size of lunar image required to satisfy the demands of maximum photographic resolution. We must not forget that the linear diameter of the Airy disc (and therefore the smallest element of resolvable detail) is proportional to the numerical value of the effective $f/$ratio of the telescope; this means that, if the size of the telescope mirror or object glass is not increased any increase in the focal length will enlarge these items by the same factor.

The 6-inch reflecting telescope, under perfect conditions, has an angular resolution of three-quarters of a second of arc; if we adopt this as the limit of resolution, and know the angular diameter of the Moon in seconds of arc, we can apply our emulsion criterion of 1,500 lines per inch to work out the required image size.

The angular diameter of the full Moon averages 1,860 seconds of arc; this can be resolved into 2,500 individual elements of detail under perfect conditions with a 6-inch; a 12-inch telescope will resolve twice as many; these must be deployed photographically to match or better the emulsion criterion if they are to be recorded. This implies an increase in the focal ratio to at least $f/32$ which, allowing some latitude and without undue prolongation of exposure, can be increased to $f/40$ (a 6-inch telescope working at $f/40$ produces lunar images exceeding 2 inches in diameter). Some workers have advocated $f/50$ as the minimum focal ratio for maximum photographic resolution. The same applies to planetary work, but whatever we do, we must not let this run us into excessively long exposures, for then what we gain in resolution upon the 'roundabouts' will be lost on the 'swings' of atmospheric turbulence.

We must aim to keep exposures short—fractions of seconds rather than seconds. Owners of non-driven telescopes should work with exposures of less than one second even if image sizes have to be reduced below the limits of maximum photographic resolution. It is much more satisfying to have sharply-defined pictures even if this is achieved at the cost of some loss of the finest detail.

But whatever we do we cannot make photographic resolution equal that of the eye. For one thing, the eye does not enlarge point images, as does the photographic emulsion. Taking a portion of the Moon containing varying gradations of light and shade, it is impossible to give each area just the requisite amount of exposure it needs. Thus the disc images of points in the brighter areas will be somewhat larger than those of the darker and less exposed portions. The brighter ones will tend to overlap the darker ones, and some confusion of the finest detail will result.

In my 35mm. astro-camera, the largest whole-disc lunar images are about one inch across. With near-perfect 'seeing', slightly under-exposed and under-developed negatives have yielded extremely detailed, if rather flat, views of the Moon.

As long as exposures are not inordinately prolonged, there is no reason why greatly magnified photographic views of the lunar surface should not be taken. This will improve the proportion of the image-size to grain-size, but in my experience magnification of the image does not lead to an increase in definition, but the reverse.

The reason for this unexpected deterioration is to be found in the supplementary lenses used for the enlargement of the image at the prime focus. The Barlow lens used for smaller images was a central component of a telephoto camera lens achromatized for the blue-violet end of the spectrum, whereas the $\frac{1}{2}$-inch eyepiece used for highly magnified views was not corrected for photographic work. This is where the Cassegrain scores over the Newtonian; for it is completely achromatic and, having a long focal length, produces larger focal plane images.

In the long run it is expedient to leave the enlarging to the dark-room and concentrate upon obtaining first-class images of moderate size, with short exposures and fine-grain emulsions.

(6) Film Speed

To get the best results we must always use emulsions of high resolution—the so-called thin emulsions. Kodak Panatomic-X, Ilford Pan F, Adox KB14 and Gevapan 27 Microgran are some of these. Slower and more contrasty emulsions are used for micro-copying, and include Kodak Microfile Pan, Ilford Microneg Pan, Gevaert Duplo Pan and a number of others. These are suitable for full Moon work—for example, with a 6-inch $f/8$ reflector, prime focal lunar images need only 1/10 second on Kodak Microfile Pan. Images of the full Moon one inch in diameter require about $\frac{1}{2}$-second exposures on the same material.

Very slow films, such as the last three, yield excellent results with continuous tone subjects—the full Moon for example. Kodak Microfile, at its fastest, has a very steep characteristic curve which can be moderated by various means but only by sacrificing speed. Since this tends to prolong exposures even more, we must switch to faster emulsions (such as the first four) for the other phases.

For the crescent phase we need emulsions with adequate exposure latitude, the slope of whose characteristic curves is not so steep. Ideally, all the varying exposure times necessary for recording all portions of the crescent should be accommodated by the straight working portion of the characteristic curve. With very steep curves the exposure latitude is insufficient—the lunar limb or the terminator could be correctly exposed, but not both. A fully-exposed terminator would involve gross over-exposure, with attendant loss of detail, in other areas.

When using micro-copying film for astronomical work, it is unnecessary to employ maximum energy developers—contrast is sufficient without them. Kodak Microfile yields good lunar negatives; I developed mine for 10 minutes at 20° C. in neat Ilford Microphen.

(7) Length of Exposure

Having decided on the image size and chosen a suitable emulsion, we are confronted with the knotty problem of determining the correct exposure.

There are two main approaches to this. The first, for the mathematically minded amateur, is the theoretical method. The effective candle-power of the lunar image must first be derived from the Moon's magnitude and colour index, allowance being made for 'seeing' and the transmission factor of the telescope. This, plus emulsion characteristics, plus much cerebral activity will ultimately reveal the necessary exposure for a given image size.

For the non-mathematical astronomical photographer there is the practical approach, which involves the empirical determination of the correct exposure. 35mm. film, by virtue of its comparatively low cost, is well suited for experimental work, and a few practice shots at various shutter speeds will soon settle the problem of exposure. It is hoped that the diagrams in this book will be some guide to correct exposures on the Moon and planets, but since no two telescopes perform identically this can be no more than approximate.

Exposure meters and Photometers

It would be most convenient if the astronomical photographer could gauge the length of his exposures by reading the light values indicated by some easily contrived exposure meter or photometer that could be plugged into the draw-tube of his telescope.

Unfortunately, with the exception of that of the Sun, the light received from all of the other celestial bodies is far too faint to be measured on simple apparatus. On the other hand, good results attend the use of more elaborate apparatus much of which lends itself to amateur construction.

Extinction meters, so-called, rely upon the ability of the eye to discern when the image is completely blacked-out by a calibrated optical wedge or stepped wedge, and are subject to considerable errors. Equal-intensity photometers, in which the light from the object is matched to a calibrated source, are of more practical value as long as the colours of the two images are roughly the same. The flicker photometer avoids this problem by presenting the two light sources to the eye in quick succession. In this way the eye does not discern colour differences and 'null' point is reached by adjusting the local source so as to give least 'flicker'.

Whenever the eye is used to judge extinction or 'null' points, it must be borne in mind that the spectral response of the eye is vastly different from that of the photographic emulsion.

Blue-sensitive photo-multiplier tubes, such as the famous 931A, are more spectrally suited for photographic work, and can be converted into sensitive and reliable photometers. Their main drawback is that they need about 1,000 volts D.C. for their dynodes and anode: derived from batteries this can be costly—and lethal! Mains power supplies are cheaper and simple to build, but unless more complicated stabilized systems are used, they are not so reliable as batteries.

Having got some type of photometer—and this is not essential— it must be calibrated. Few readers will have access to standard light sources and the best method of calibration is therefore to make a careful note of the photometer reading before each exposure. Some sort of pattern for future exposures will soon emerge. All readings, exposures attempted, results and all relevant detail, including developing and processing, must be carefully noted if the scheme is to succeed.

Subtle differences exist between the photo-electric and visual types of exposure meter, and unless allowance is made the readings can be unreliable. The photo-electric meter integrates all the light received from the object whereas the visual type is capable of measuring the intensity of selected portions of the object. For example, a photo-electric photometer will register a decline in light

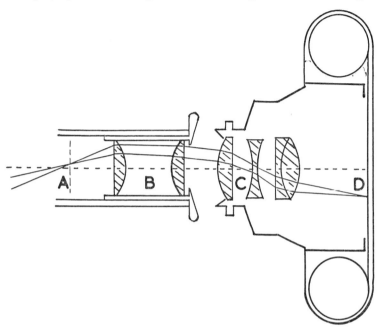

FIG. 9

Telescopic work with 'ordinary' cameras

Light rays forming an image in the Newtonian focal plane, A, diverge and enter the positive eyepiece, B, to be emitted parallel—the telescope being in normal adjustment. They then fall on the camera lens, C, adjusted for infinity. An erect image will then be formed in the plane of the emulsion at D.

intensity during the partial stages of a solar eclipse. The visual instrument will indicate no such change, for the visible part of the Sun is just as bright as ever, and no reduction of exposure will be necessary. The photo-electric photometer, in this case, is register-ing the reduced effective area of the solar disc and not a light-change. Daylight coming in with that of the object can also lead to erroneous exposure factors.

Commercial Cameras

As an aid to accurate focusing when using commercial cameras at the telescope,[1] a small hand telescope can be pressed into service. This is first focused precisely upon the Moon—*i.e.*, is focused effectively for infinity. It is then pointed into the eyepiece of the large telescope, which is also pointed at the Moon. If a clear view of a small but highly-enlarged portion of the lunar surface is observed through both telescopes, all is well: the larger instrument is also properly focused for parallel light. But if the image is out of focus, the eyepiece must be moved in or out until this is corrected. The adjustment of the small telescope must not, of course, be altered after the initial setting.

The camera, with its lens set at infinity, is then pointed squarely into the eyepiece of the larger telescope, and an accurately focused lunar image will fall on the emulsion when the shutter is released. Nevertheless, it may be found that the developed image is blurred. All-over lack of definition probably indicates incorrect setting of the camera-lens to infinity and may necessitate the recalibration of the engraved distance settings upon the lens ring. If the image is blurred in one direction only, the cause is probably camera shake.

Commercial cameras with removable lenses—the Leica is a famous example—can be used to receive prime focal and enlarged images from the telescope direct. Focusing can be done with special attachments obtainable from the makers. Spare camera-backs are sometimes available—if so, high-power focusing eyepieces can be fixed to these, as in my astro-camera. Mr. C. A. Swindin of Bristol has made this modification to a French Foca camera which is very similar to the Leica, and the excellent results procured fully justify the alteration.

[1] It must always be remembered that long sight and, to an even greater extent, short-sight, will introduce focusing errors. Many observers remove spectacles while working at the telescope.

Single lens reflex cameras also provide easy means of focusing and of selecting the desired region of the lunar surface. If the lens is removable, so much the better, for the camera becomes more versatile. Some of the older reflex cameras suffer from camera shake when the shutters are released—so be warned.

Using the Astronomical Camera

Focusing presents no difficulties with the 35mm. astronomical camera which has already been described in some detail. The sequence of operations is included here as a guide to those with similar equipment. It is assumed the film has been loaded and perforated with a punch, and that the camera is sealed against the light.

(1) The camera is plugged into the draw-tube of the telescope (which may contain supplementary lenses to provide a magnified image).

(2) With the shutter release and the shutter set to 'Time', open the latter to admit light into the camera. The prismatic eyepiece is withdrawn to Position 2, out of the way of the incoming light.

(3) The 'keyhole cover' over the positive eyepiece at the back of the camera is moved to one side. The operator's view through the eyepiece and the hole in the film will be a confusion of light, or nothing at all, depending on the setting of the object in the field. If nothing is seen, adjust R.A. and Declination of telescope.

(4) Adjust the telescope's draw-tube to give a sharply defined view in the focusing eyepiece.

(5) Lock the camera to the telescope to preserve this setting against accidental movement.

(6) Press release to close shutter. Cover focusing eyepiece. The camera is thus sealed against light.

(7) Wind film to frame 2 (Frame 1 was perforated for focusing).

(8) Select the object to be photographed with the 'prismatic eyepiece', or failing that, with a long focus guide telescope.

(9) *a.* Set the chosen shutter speed, *or*

b. Cover upper end of telescope with flap-type shutter and open the camera's shutter or slide.

(10) Allow all vibration to cease—count up to ten. Then:

a. Release the metal-leaved shutter by means of the flexible cable, *or*

b. Swing the flap-type shutter (which has been edged away from the upper end of the telescope) rapidly sideways, replacing it after the estimated exposure time has elapsed. The camera is sealed by shutter or slide again.

(11) Wind on film to frame 3.

(12) Check that the object is still within the field of the camera before attempting further exposures. If the prismatic eyepiece or the more traditional reflex arrangement is used, remember to remove it afterwards.

3. An enlarged portion of the Moon, showing the formations Clavius, Tycho and the Straight Wall. April 19th, 1955. 6-inch reflector plus Barlow lens working at $f/30$. Film, Kodak Panatomic-X. Exposure, 1 second. The image of Tycho is 1 mm across on the negative.

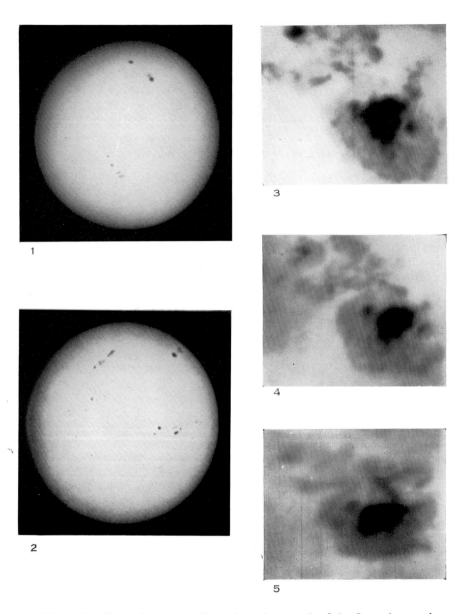

4. The Solar disc and sunspots. No. 1 is a photograph of the Sun taken at the Newtonian focus through a silvered 'lantern-slide' type filter. Film, Ilford Positive Fine-grain safety film. Exposure, 1/100 second. August 3rd, 1957. The largest sunspot in No. 1 is shown in close-up in Nos. 3, 4 and 5, which reveal its development during three consecutive days. These were obtained by the last method outlined in Chapter 6 No. 2 is a whole disc record obtained by photographing the projected solar image on a card screen. June 20th, 1957.

CHAPTER 6

Photographing the Sun

The intensity of the Sun's light and heat is a serious obstacle which has to be surmounted before satisfactory views can be procured either visually or photographically. The object glass or mirror of a telescope collects all the parallel solar rays incident upon it and refracts or reflects them to the focal plane of the telescope. Blindness will result if the observer tries to view the Sun through his telescope without adequate protection. Even with the protection of a neutral filter there is still much heat to reckon with—enough to crack the filter, perhaps damaging the eye with pieces of broken glass.

Photographic emulsions also react violently to solar light and heat—the problem is to reduce their intensity to a reasonable level.

Methods for controlling Solar light and heat

For the specialist in solar studies a suitable reflecting telescope could be constructed embodying the usual primary and secondary mirrors but with no silver or aluminium films. About 96% of the solar rays will pass through the primary mirror and only 4% will be reflected to the secondary mirror; this in turn will only reflect 4% of the light impinging upon it. The brightness of the image formed in the focal plane will therefore be reduced to something like one five-hundredth of that of the 'aluminized' image. Heating is also reduced, and the solar image is nearer to photographic requirements, although filters may still have to be used.

Most amateurs are nocturnal creatures—or at any rate diurnal—and prefer to have their optical surfaces metal-coated, so that they can be used to reflect the fainter objects of the night sky. Let us consider some of the ways of reducing the efficiency of such telescopes so that they can be safely employed for solar work.

The easiest way is to use an eccentric stop or diaphragm fitted to the upper end of the reflecting telescope—with refractors the stop can be centrally fixed. This is simply a piece of cardboard with a round aperture cut in it. The eccentric aperture, in the case of a reflector, allows the light entering the instrument to avoid the diagonal flat mirror and the supporting web.

Though easy to arrange, this method cannot be recommended, as only a small portion of the primary mirror is used, and the resolution of the telescope is very seriously reduced. About one square inch of aluminized surface will reflect as much light as the whole area of an uncoated 6-inch mirror—the latter preserving its original powers of resolution. An aperture of one square inch corresponds to a hole 1·13 inches diameter and a limiting visual resolution (using Dawes' criterion) of about four seconds of arc, whereas the resolution threshold of the 6-inch mirror is about three-quarters of a second.

Enlarged pictures of sunspots may be attempted with the same apparatus as that used for lunar close-ups; but with reduced aperture and a positive eyepiece there is every likelihood of spurious

---

FIG. 10

Six methods of reducing solar light and heat

1. *Nearly opaque silver-on-glass filter covering the upper end of the telescope.*
2. *Asymmetrical diaphragm for reducing aperture. Three springy strips hold it to the inside or outside of the tube.*
3. *Solar diagonal, or Herschel wedge. Most of the light and heat passes through it. The 4% reflection can be further reduced with filters, as at F.*
4. *In this case, polarized light reflected from the unsilvered surface passes through a crossed polaroid filter, P, before reaching the camera. The back surface of the glass can be 'bloomed' or frosted, or shaped as in 3 to reduce back reflections.*

130

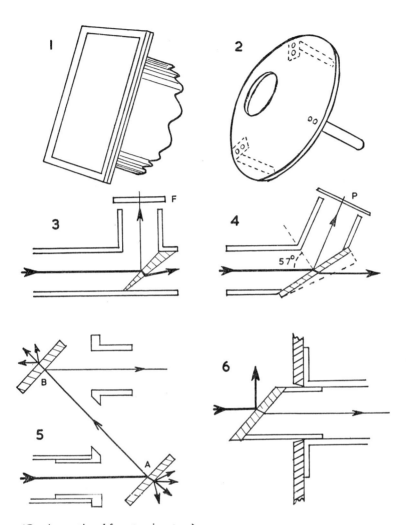

(Caption continued from previous page)

5. Two reflections from unsilvered glass mirrors reduce the glare about six-hundred fold. The back surfaces are frosted to break up unwanted reflections.
6. A front-silvered flat intercepts light and heat in front of the draw-tube and reflects them out of the end of the telescope. It should be possible to see a blue solar image through the silver film.

sunspots being recorded. Each blemish and speck of dust on the lenses of the eyepiece will show up on the photograph. A Barlow lens is less affected by such troubles. Other difficulties arise with the focusing, for where large f/ratios are employed, the rays converge at such slight angles that it is difficult to ascertain the precise focus.

As so often happens in astronomical photography we must compromise. Excessively small apertures, like our 1-inch diaphragm, yield poor images. Proportional improvement will attend the use of larger apertures of, say, two or three inches diameter. A 2-inch eccentric diaphragm will use as much of one side of a 6-inch telescope mirror as is possible without encroaching upon the region masked by the diagonal. This will also give a visual resolution limit of about two-seconds of arc, which is a good deal better than the atmosphere will allow much of the time.

To reduce the light still further on its way to the camera, some modification of the solar wedge can be used. The solar wedge is a narrow wedge of glass through which most of the Sun's light and heat passes. The remaining 4% is reflected from an optically-worked face into the observer's eyepiece or camera, while the rest passes out through the end of the draw-tube. Reflections from the back face do not interfere with the observer, since this face is not inclined at 45° to the axis of the incident light. The device should be used with due caution, for the unwanted heat emerging from the end of the draw-tube may set fire to clothing or cause painful burns.

Yet another idea involves the use of a parallel glass flat, silvered on one side and mounted on the upper end of the telescope, and sufficiently large to cover the whole mirror. The snag here is expense, for large, optically-worked flats are extremely costly. I compromised by using two pieces of selected Pilkington plate glass; one of these was silvered to an estimated 90% and the two pieces were made into a large 'lantern slide'—that is, bound round the edges with sticky tape, the silvered surface being inside. The Sun's disc can be seen through it without glare, and is blue in colour.

Fixed over the upper end of the 6-inch reflector, this filter very effectively removes the bulk of the light and heat by simply reflecting it back at the Sun. By this means the disc could be examined in the eyepiece of the telescope without additional filters and excessive glare and, what is more important, without danger to the eye. Whole disc photography with this apparatus was also successful.

If a large unsilvered optical flat is available it can be mounted on the upper end of the tube and its angle adjusted to reflect the Sun's light into the telescope. The flat would have to be very large to cover all of the 6-inch mirror, but part of the telescope mirror could be diaphragmed off as before. As with the solar wedge, the introduction of a third reflecting surface reverses the image.

Polarizing devices also offer scope for the experimenter. Reflection polarizers are better for solar work than transmission polarizers (such as Polaroid) since the latter can be rapidly destroyed by the Sun's heat concentrated in the draw-tube.

At the draw-tube end of the telescope, residual light can be further reduced by filters, providing that most of the heat has been removed first. Special heat-absorbing glasses are manufactured at Messrs. Chance-Pilkington Optical Works.

Yet another method involves an inclined front-silvered mirror intercepting the solar rays just before they enter the draw-tube and deflecting most of them out of the upper end of the telescope. It can be made from a selected piece of polished plate (not less than about an eighth of an inch thick), and is silvered until the blue solar image can be seen through the coating without glare. There is no need to burnish the film.

Care should be taken to ensure that no part of the instrument is damaged; a slight displacement of the mirror may allow the cone of rays to miss the diagonal altogether, and they may burn the tube or the diaphragm at the upper end. A conflagration was narrowly averted in my own telescope on one occasion: it would be most demoralizing to see one's telescope tube smoking like a factory chimney.

Apart from the specialist's unaluminized telescope, it can be appreciated that the normal 6-inch reflector is really too big for solar work—at least, as far as light grasp goes, though its resolving power is still valuable. Resolution is always desirable, but in my opinion a 3- or 4-inch telescope will usually show all the solar detail that the atmosphere will allow. This means that amateurs with quite small telescopes can do useful work, both visually and photographically, without motor-drives or even equatorial mountings.

Solar Photography

One of the easiest, most convenient and safest ways of viewing the Sun is to project its image upon a white card supported some distance away from a low-power eyepiece in the draw-tube. The image is bright and large and any sunspots or maculae present are well shown. There is no difficulty in photographing the card screen with an ordinary commercial camera providing its lens can be focused for short distances—if it cannot, a supplementary lens may be placed in front of it, and the camera lens set at infinity. Supplementary lenses of 18-inches and upwards focal lengths can be bought, or odd anastigmatic spectacle lenses can be suitably mounted and used. The camera must be mounted firmly and accurately at whatever distance is chosen.

The solar image projected straight on to a ground glass screen cannot be successfully photographed by a camera placed behind it. Being translucent, the screen not only displays the solar image but also transmits direct light from the eyepiece; furthermore, any blemish or accidental smear upon the screen will be very much in evidence. Photographing the projected image from the front is best, even if the image is reversed; this can be corrected in the darkroom.

Another method employs a totally reflecting prism or, failing that, a front-surfaced plane mirror, either of which can be fixed to the outside of the draw-tube or adjacent metal-work. The commercial camera can be pointed into this to secure views of the white card screen—not only will the solar images come out the

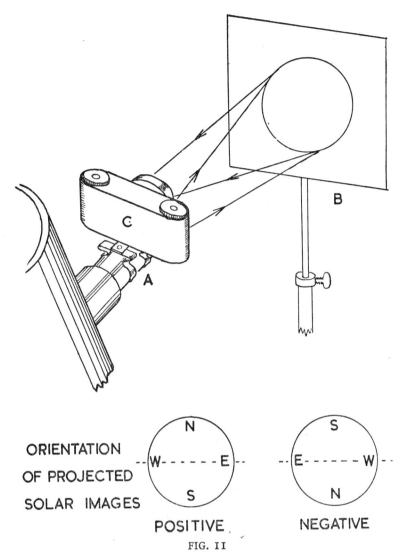

ORIENTATION
OF PROJECTED
SOLAR IMAGES

POSITIVE

NEGATIVE

FIG. II

A simple and safe method for whole disc photography.

A projected solar image from the draw-tube, A, falls on the white screen, B. The miniature camera, C, clipped to the draw-tube, records the solar image. Delayed action and flexible cable release help to minimise vibration. Low power projection lenses and eyepieces must be used to overcome serious parallax troubles.

Projected solar images are shown as they face the camera, the East-West line being always parallel to the optical axis of the primary mirror. The type of projection lens used is indicated below each diagram.

right way round, but there will be less trouble from parallax. The latter will be more evident with other methods where the commercial camera has to peer round the barrel of the telescope tube at the screen.

Slow emulsions can be used with this super-abundance of light, and their contrast characteristics also help to emphasize fainter detail. Sunspots appear dark only in comparison with the rest of the solar disc; they are really very bright objects, and there is no violent contrast between them and the disc as viewed upon the projection screen. Smaller and fainter ones often escape detection but are sometimes made visible to the eye by vibrating the telescope. Contrasty emulsions help to bring out these elusive objects —also any non-solar markings, so that an absolutely clean screen is essential.

Cameras must be treated with due respect in bright sunlight. Chinks and slits and tiny holes in the bellows will admit enough light to spoil even slow film very quickly. Leave nothing to chance and always keep the camera shielded from direct sunlight.

Exposure times can be derived by experiment or by taking readings upon an exposure meter. A photo-electric meter held close to the screen will give a good indication of the required exposure. Even so, it is wise also to use shutter settings on either side of the calculated one. A note of the details of every exposure must be made.

A simple method that I have used for sunspot close-ups is to project a large solar image via a low-power eyepiece on to the screen, as before. Here the image can be examined, and interesting areas selected for photography. No additional lenses or draw-tubes are required, and any camera can be used so long as the clear aperture of the open shutter, without camera lenses, is large enough to admit the image of the chosen object. Focal plane shutters are more suitable than metal-leaved types, and a Leica camera without its lenses is ideal for the purpose. The camera must be shielded from direct sunlight: it can, for instance, be placed within a cardboard or wooden box one side of which has been removed. The camera is held steady in front of the telescope draw-tube, and the pre-focused image enters the protective box and falls squarely on the closed camera shutter, which is then operated by cable release.

I have obtained good views of sunspots by this method, using Ilford Fine Grain Safety Positive film with exposures of 1/25 to 1/50 second. Slower speeds, as well as producing over-exposed negatives, lead to fogging from stray light, while faster speeds with metal-leaved shutters cause undesirable shutter patterns. The measured size of the full solar image was 15½ inches, and I confess that, disregarding the frowns of the theoreticians, I reduced the aperture of the telescope to 1¾ inches with an eccentric diaphragm, thus producing the prodigious focal ratio of 900. This implies shutter speeds of the order of 1/1,000 second for medium speed emulsions at $f/450$ which would seem to indicate that $f/64$, advocated by Waters and others, is far too small a focal ratio.

Focal plane shutters are valuable because they allow shorter, 'turbulence freezing' exposures to be made with larger telescope apertures, thereby yielding an all-round improvement of definition.

The telescope must not be allowed to accept the Sun's light at full (6-inch) aperture for more than a few seconds at a time; an accomplice can be delegated to cover the upper end of the telescope between shots.

Large images will not appreciably heat up camera shutters, but small, intense images will quickly damage cloth and rubberized focal plane and roller blind shutters. These will burn and their replacement is expensive. Flap-type shutters are too slow and 'leaky' for use with reflectors, but may be useful with refractors or when filters are used.

CHAPTER 7

Solar and Lunar Eclipse Photography

The value of eclipse photography depends on the skill of the amateur in recording these transitory events. A series of consecutively-mounted pictures will convey far more than chapters of verbal description, not only to contemporary, but also to future astronomers, perhaps centuries hence.

Total eclipses of the Sun happen fairly frequently, but usually in faraway places. The professional astronomer who wishes to observe them has to travel perhaps thousands of miles on what can easily turn out to be a futile journey if the weather is unfavourable. The suitably-equipped and located amateur should therefore make every effort to secure a photographic record of such events, and he may well succeed where his professional colleagues fail. If he happens to be situated on the track of totality or within easy distance of it—assuming it to be a total eclipse and not an annular one—he should try to obtain photographs of the solar corona, which is only to be seen under the most favourable conditions when the Sun is completely blotted out by the Moon. It needs fairly long exposures, and since its brightness is variable there is no way the amateur can predict them. During the precious moments of totality the greatest possible number of exposures must be made at a variety of shutter speeds. If no estimate of the correct exposure can be made—expose at many speeds. Whatever is done should be written down by a companion, for on these occasions nothing must be committed to memory.

Solar Telescopic Work

The image formed at the Newtonian focal plane is large enough

138

for solar eclipse work showing the progress of the Moon during the partial stages. Where fine detail is not sought, it is permissible to 'stop down' the telescope or to use some type of filter. During the solar eclipse of 1954, I photographed the partial phase through a silvered 'lantern-slide'-type filter, as described in the last chapter. The 6-inch reflector was capped by a 4-inch concentric diaphragm which also supported the filter. Images were magnified by means of a weak, chromatically-uncorrected Barlow lens to a diameter of 18mm.,[1] exposures of 1/25 second were found adequate for emulsions of moderate speed—Kodak Panatomic-X was the one actually used. (The speed of this emulsion has subsequently been reduced a little.)

The partial phase of an eclipse presents little difficulty and trial runs for determining correct exposures can be made a day or two in advance. Having determined the best exposure time for the whole disc there is no need to modify it during the partial stages, as the brightness of the visible portion of the Sun remains substantially the same—true, the solar disc is less bright at the limb, but not enough to upset exposure times.

Focal plane images are best for totality, and a 6-inch $f/8$ reflector will be able to record the solar corona. (Only the fastest, very wide aperture cameras will record the faint extensions of the corona, which often extend to distances of several solar diameters.) For once, we can employ faster emulsions: only a small degree of enlargement will be required from these negatives, and graininess will not seriously upset us—Ilford HP3 or even HPS can be used, and Newtonian focal plane image exposures of, say, 1 or 2 seconds (and even longer if possible) will record the corona and prominences. The occurrence of prominences cannot be forecast and large ones like the famous 'Anteater' prominence of 1919 are rare. It is important to realize that for photographs of the corona there is no 'correct' exposure: the longer the exposure, the greater the extent of corona that will be recorded. With very long exposures its brighter portions will necessarily be 'burnt out' or over-exposed.

---

[1] In this case the image size was increased in order to keep the diaphragm-type shutter speeds slow.

The clock reading of each exposure, if accurately recorded, gives valuable information on the progress of the eclipse—this task can be left to the photographer's companion. Precious minutes cannot be wasted by the solar eclipse photographer—his attention must be concentrated, to the exclusion of all else, on securing as many exposures as he can. Complete familiarity with the apparatus is essential, and a few dress rehearsals should be staged before the event.

Smaller cameras, of shorter focal length and wider aperture, are more portable, and if considerable distances have to be travelled to the most suitable observing location, it is more than likely these will be used in preference to larger and less transportable equipment. They should be rigidly mounted. Hand-held cameras are not recommended, although it must be conceded they sometimes yield surprisingly fine results. As an example we can cite Dr. W. H. Steavenson's[1] feat in recording the fainter extensions of the solar corona in 1954 with a 12-cm. focal length Zeiss Tessar working at $f/4.5$ and an exposure of $1/15$ second on an Ilford Selochrome plate. MacFarlane[2] and Clark have also suggested medium-speed orthochromatic emulsions and 1 second exposures at $f/4 \cdot 5$ for the outer corona.

Lunar Eclipse Photography

By their very nature, lunar eclipses are not confined to narrow strips of the terrestrial surface, and astronomers do not have to travel to remote portions of the Earth to observe them. A lunar eclipse can be observed from all parts of the Earth's hemisphere from which the Moon is visible. It does not follow that good views will be afforded from all such locations. There is much to be said in favour of setting up the telescope in the temperate to tropical regions as opposed to higher latitudes.

The appearance of the Moon at mid-eclipse—conditioned to

[1] Steavenson, W. H. (Photograph) *B.A.A. Journal*, Vol. 64, No. 8.
[2] MacFarlane and Clark. *Solar Eclipse Photography*, contained in *Amateur Telescope Making*, Book 2.

some extent by vagaries of our own atmosphere—is unpredictable. There have been occasions when observers have 'lost' the Moon completely. But generally it can be seen quite easily, the disc being of a reddish colour.

These eclipses are very much longer than solar ones and can be conveniently divided into three distinct phases. First the penumbral shadow crosses the disc—often this is barely detectable. Then comes the umbral shadow, leading to mid-eclipse, preceded and followed by the partial phases. Lastly the following part of the penumbra crosses the Moon. The whole sequence of events takes several hours.

A 6-inch reflecting telescope is an ideal instrument for lunar eclipse photography. Focal plane images are large enough, and medium-speed emulsions can be used. Exposures must be increased in length to offset the diminution of light as the umbra commences to cover the lunar disc. Nor must atmospheric factors be neglected, due allowance being made for any light haze or ground mist. In such cases—as always when exposure factors are in doubt—it is safest to use a variety of shutter speeds.

As with solar work, the programme should be well planned in advance, and if a companion is available to take notes, so much the better. The visual observation of a lunar eclipse is a long and tiring task, but well worth the effort. Anything unusual should of course be carefully noted. At mid-eclipse it is interesting to make long exposures, in the hope of recording the darkened disc. For these, the telescope must be guided. The crater Aristarchus, the brightest on the Moon, can sometimes be seen after the others have disappeared; if it is visible the telescope can be guided on it for the duration of the exposure. It is useless to guide on a star, because of the Moon's motion.

Since the duration of the mid-eclipse varies, and it is impossible to forecast the brightness of the totally eclipsed Moon, a series of long exposures should be undertaken. A suggested programme would include one, five, ten and perhaps fifteen minute exposures on medium-speed red sensitive emulsions. At first sight it would appear that total solar and lunar eclipses have much in common, but in fact the reverse is the case. With solar work, there is no time for long exposures at totality and even if there were, we should have nothing to guide the telescope on.

The Earthlit Moon

Using the same techniques, the amateur can try his hand at photographing the earthlit Moon. The sunlit crescent will be greatly over-exposed—no film has the exposure latitude demanded by such an object. A guided telescope at $f/8$ will record the earthlit area in about one minute on medium speed panchromatic materials (I have used Kodak Panatomic-X successfully).

Good guiding presupposes an efficient driving mechanism and smooth manually-operated slow motions. A good long focus-guiding telescope is to be preferred to 'beam splitting' devices which deflect some of the light from the camera to the guiding eyepiece—this necessitates increased exposures which can be ill-afforded, particularly during eclipses.

CHAPTER 8

Planetary Photography

In Chapter 1, the apparent sizes of the planets were compared with those of the Sun and Moon, and they were found to have much smaller angular diameters. Nevertheless, given good atmospheric conditions, the amateur can use his 6-inch reflector to obtain photographs of them. In recent years, there has been more optimism regarding planetary photography among amateurs. As so often happens, no one knows what can be done until someone tries a thing and shows that it is possible—with results that sometimes surprise the theoreticians.

Image Sizes

All the planets, without exception, must have their focal plane images enlarged. The diameter of Jupiter's image in the focal plane of a 6-inch $f/8$ telescope is about a quarter of a millimetre. This is obviously a good deal too small—not only will much of the detail be lost in the diffusion of the emulsion, but a twelve-fold enlargement in the darkroom will produce a print only three millimetres, or one-eighth of an inch, across. Larger images are desirable to exploit the photographic resolution of the telescope and to minimize losses of detail due to diffusion. Nor must we go to the other extreme and magnify the focal plane image so much that we run into the troubles connected with excessively long exposures, coupled with guiding and turbulence difficulties. In the interest of the finer detail focal ratios of not less than $f/40$ should be used— I have frequently used $f/90$, still with reasonably short exposures.

Magnifying Planetary Images

Barlow lenses and telenegative lenses are to be preferred when low magnifications are required. Positive eyepieces of short focal length yield greatly enlarged images, usually at the expense of marginal definition. With planetary work, this last is of no great importance as long as the image is kept near the centre of the field. Achromatic oculars are essential if fine detail is to be recorded. My favourite eyepiece for this work is a half-inch orthoscopic (giving a magnification of $\times 96$), but higher powers have been used on occasion.

The Brightness of Planetary Images

The dominant factor—controlling the size of the image on the emulsion, the choice of film, and the length of exposure—is the photographic brightness of the planets. This is not the same as the visual brightness. Without exception, all the planetary discs within the range of our 6-inch telescope are fainter to the photographic plate than they are to the eye. The same is true of the Sun and Moon. The more balanced colour sensitivity of modern panchromatic emulsions reduces, but does not nullify, this effect.

The visual brightness of a planet depends upon its distance from the Sun, its distance from the Earth, its phase, and the nature of the visible surface, be it solid, as in the case of Mars, or gaseous like Jupiter and Saturn. At opposition, the superior planets are well placed for observation in the midnight sky, and at the same time are at their closest. These favourable occasions can be determined and exploited for photography by referring to the B.A.A. *Handbook* and other ephemerides.

Reliable estimates of photographic brightness are difficult to find but some idea of the brightness relationships can be derived from the visual magnitudes and colour indices. Taking the exposure time for Venus as unity, the corresponding values for Jupiter, Mars and Saturn are found to be in the proportions 6·5, 10 and 30 respectively. These figures are not applicable to panchro-

5. The solar eclipse of June 30th, 1954. Photographed at Cambridge through high cirrus clouds. Exposure, 1/25 second. Film, Kodak Panatomic-X (26° B.S.I.). Silvered glass, 'lantern-slide' type filter. 6-inch reflector stopped down to 4 inches, equivalent to f/24.

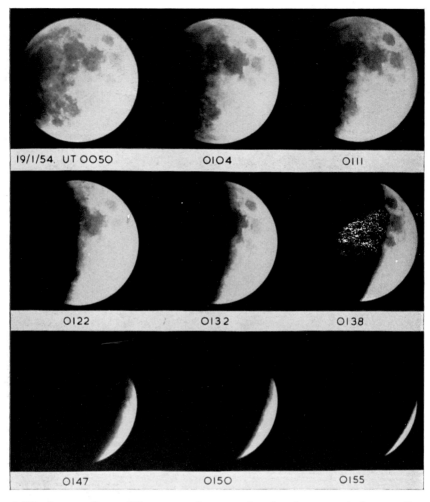

19/1/54. UT 0050   0104   0111

0122   0132   0138

0147   0150   0155

6. The lunar eclipse of January 19th, 1954, showing the stages before totality. Exposures, $\frac{1}{8}$-second to 20 seconds at $f/13$. Film, Adox KB14 (23° B.S.I.).

7. Nos. 1 and 2 illustrate the rapid motion of Comet Arend-Roland against the starry background. Consecutive exposures, of 10 and 15 minutes respectively, on Kodak Panatomic-X. Newtonian focal plane images. Developed in Promicrol, 1:1 dilution, 18 minutes, 20° C. April 28th, 1957.

Nos. 3, 4 and 5 show Jupiter on March 9th and April 5th and 6th, 1956. The shadow of the satellite Ganymede appears on No. 3. There are two satellite shadows on No. 4, but that of Io is too close to the gibbous esatern limb of the planet to be clearly identified.

Mars is depicted in Nos. 6, 7 and 8. Dates: September 13th and 17th and October 13th, 1956, respectively.

No. 9, an ultra-violet photograph of the planet before opposition, shows the prominent southern polar cap. July 27th, 1956.

No. 10: Saturn, May 7th, 1954. Declination, approximately 11° S. It will not be well placed for northern observers until 1966.

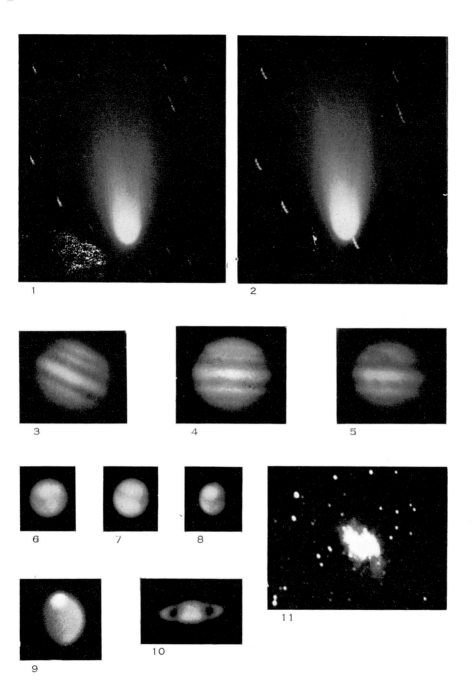

In a small telescope it is a mistake to enlarge planetary images too much. A 3 mm image is sufficient for Jupiter, and 2 mm images suffice for Mars and Saturn with medium to fast emulsions.

No. 11: the Crab Nebula. Exposure, 90 minutes; otherwise conditions identical with Nos. 1 and 2. February 16th, 1957. The image of this faint object is 1 mm across on the negative. A second negative was used to improve the contrast.

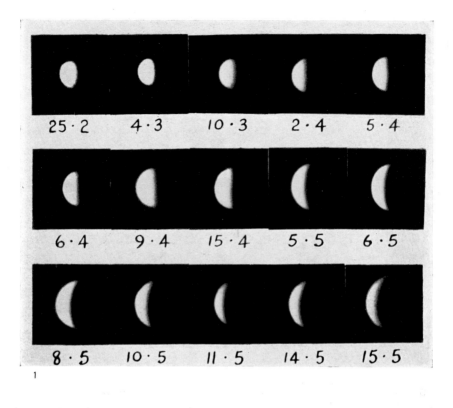

1

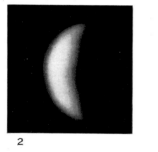

2

3

8. No. 1: part of 1956 Venus sequence (visible light). No. 2 shows typical ultra-violet markings largely shown as indentations in the terminator. May 5th, 1956. No. 3 shows a portion of the lunar surface photographed with a Voigtlander Vito II held at the eyepiece of the 6-inch reflector magnifying 60 times. Ilford HP3, exposure 1/25 second. September 17th, 1956.

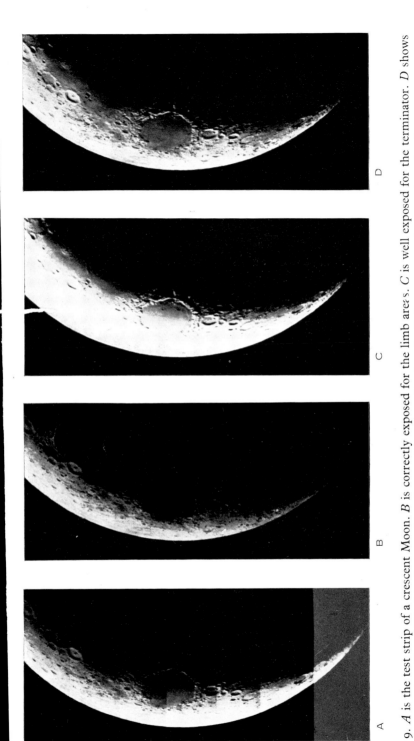

9. *A* is the test strip of a crescent Moon. *B* is correctly exposed for the terminator. *D* shows the effect of 'dodging', or masking the terminator, so allowing the limb areas to register on the enlarging paper.

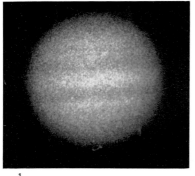

1

2

3

10. No. 1 shows the objectionable graininess that results from over-enlargement. No. 2, obtained by combining sixteen images of Jupiter, reveals more planetary detail and far less graininess. No. 3 is a focal plane photograph of the Moon taken on December 18th, 1956. Exposure 1/10 second, Kodak Microfile Pan. Developed in Promicrol, 1:1 dilution, for 5 minutes at 20° C. The diameter of the image on the negative is approaching $\frac{1}{2}$ inch.

matic emulsions. Saturn is a special case—its brightness varies over wide limits according to the degree of opening of the rings. Jupiter is the most stable, its actinic brightness only varying slightly. The apparent brightness and angular diameters of Venus and Mars vary widely as they approach and recede from the Earth. In the absence of sensitive and accurate photometers—not generally included in amateur apparatus—it is better to determine the correct exposure by experiment. A few shots at different shutter speeds are always the most reliable guide to photographic conduct.

Choice of Film

The problem resolves itself thus: is it preferable to use moderate-sized images with slower, contrasty and virtually grainless emulsions, or larger, light-starved images and extremely fast film? The former alternative involves more enlargement in the darkroom, but this is generally to be preferred to using very high magnifications in the telescope.

From the point of view of graininess, there seems little to choose between them. A small image on a medium-speed emulsion, if enlarged to the same size as a large image on a fast emulsion, will show about the same degree of graininess.

The most important—to my mind the decisive—factor in favour of slower emulsions is that of contrast. Of our two otherwise identical enlargements, the one obtained from the slower emulsion will show planetary detail more clearly: it will have a greater range of tones than the photograph obtained from the faster emulsion, and contrast, as indicated by the slope of the characteristic curve, greatly influences the resolution of an emulsion.

Mees[1] states, 'If the resolving power is to be high, the characteristics of the emulsion must be such that the images will become sufficiently dense to outline the narrow lines before the intervening spaces fill up; in other words, gamma must be high and turbidity low.'

As we have seen, we cannot get high γ values from fast emul-

[1] Mees, C. E. K. *The Theory of Photographic Process.*

sions, with their gentle sloping curves. To combat the effects of turbidity, manufacturers have produced 'thin' emulsions of moderate speed and reasonably high contrast. These are less affected by diffusion and are strongly to be recommended for astronomical work.

At their best, planetary markings do not exhibit a wide range of tonal values, and it must be the photographer's aim to exaggerate contrast—to produce a negative that, as regards tone, is 'larger than life'. This is where we depart from ordinary pictorial and portrait work. Few sitters would enthuse over portraits showing their facial defects much enhanced; most portrait workers, on the contrary, try to remove the blemishes so as to flatter the sitter. Not so the planetary worker. His job is to make the 'facial defects' as plain as conditions and equipment will allow.

This will be facilitated by using the slower, 'thin' emulsions; these will record contrast on the negative, so that it will not have to be manufactured in the darkroom, as it can be by a suitable choice of printing papers. Flat negatives, lacking in contrast, are the product of fast emulsions, with their attendant graininess. When these are printed in the darkroom, the contrasty papers used for making enlarged positives enhance not only the picture detail but also the graininess.

There are methods for dealing with graininess, as we shall see, but if we can avoid it in the first place it is much better to do so—especially when the time factor is important.

All the precautions observed in recording the Moon apply equally to planetary work. Focusing, a fussy business at the best of times, should be given even more meticulous attention than usual. Once the correct position has been found for the camera, lock it against accidental movement. Allow all vibration to cease before exposing. Do not forget the cable release for the shutter. Remember to remove any prismatic eyepiece or reflex mirror before taking the picture. If 'seeing' conditions are not good, do not waste film—return indoors and do some enlarging.

The Furthest Planets

So much for the nearer and larger planets. Uranus, Neptune and Pluto do not present the photographer with large enough discs, and Mercury is too near the Sun. A well-driven telescope can record the positions of these three superior planets, and a succession of photographs taken over a period of days or weeks will show the displacement of the planet against the background stars.

Pluto, the faintest and furthest of the planets, also travels the most slowly, taking about three weeks to cross half a degree of sky, or, roughly, one full Moon's width. This apparent movement is due more to the Earth's motion than to that of Pluto itself. Neptune behaves in a similar way, while the motion of Uranus, when near opposition, is approximately twice as rapid as the two outer planets. Focal plane photographs of the star-fields known to include these bodies will reveal them. If the prime focal image of Uranus, in our 6-inch $f/8$ telescope, is allowed to trail across a medium-speed emulsion, its path will be revealed upon development. Kodak Panatomic-X was used for this experiment, and showed that Uranus can be recorded in about one second. Unfortunately, it often happens that the planet is the brightest object in the field and longer exposures have to be given to supply a few stellar reference points.

A slight digression here: since Uranus is of about the sixth magnitude, it follows that most of the stars visible to the unaided eye, other than the less actinic red ones, can be recorded in approximately one second. This is not true of extended objects.

When using aluminized surfaces, without lenses and eyepieces, advantage is taken of the highly actinic ultra-violet region of the spectrum as far as the atmospheric 'cut-off'. Thus the telescope is a good deal faster photographically than visually.

Neptune's image will require rather longer, but exposures of ten seconds will record it under similar conditions.

Pluto (photographic magnitude 15), is most elusive and the photographer must prepare himself for a guiding vigil of over one hour if he is to record this remote object. Guiding can be broken up into shorter spells with a few minutes' rest in between. Comfort is important and, if absent, the need for it increases logarithmically with time.

Minor Planets

Minor planets can be detected in like manner. Some of them come close to the Earth, and when they do their proper motions against the starry backgrounds are rapid enough for them to be recorded as trails upon photographic emulsions guided on the stars. If the planet is bright enough, the telescope can be guided on it for the duration of the exposure, and the stars will trail instead. Successful exposures depend wholly upon the equipment, accurate guiding, and the patience of the observer.

Comets

Comets are exciting objects to photograph—especially the rarer and brighter ones. The nucleus of such a comet should be used for guiding. In this way, good clear shots of it can be obtained at the Newtonian focus. At the same time, the telescope should be encumbered with as many wide aperture, short focal length cameras as it will hold without upsetting its balance. These will record the fainter regions of the tail—perhaps over a large area of sky. Guiding is made more difficult by the fact that it has to be done in both R.A. and Declination, and if the comet's head is vague and ill-defined, this adds to the photographer's troubles. Ordinary cross-hairs can be used in the eyepiece of the guiding telescope but I have found it easier to guide if the comet's image is not bisected but held in one of the corners made by the cross hairs. Dr. W. H. Steavenson advocates a small, metal, spire-like triangle upon the apex of which the image of the comet is impaled 'like a toffee-apple on a stick'.

Exact times and all relevant instrumental data of every photograph should be recorded.

Nebulae and Star Clusters

Many of the larger and brighter nebulae and star clusters are well within the range of a 6-inch telescope. Patience and persistence on the operator's part, and a well-mounted telescope with an efficient drive and slow motions are the essentials. There are no rules concerning exposures—the photographer just carries on as long as he is able. Given a really dark, moonless night and a telescope working at $f/8$ fogging of the film by sky light is not likely to occur in under eight hours. Few observers would be prepared to guide the telescope for as long as this, and here we touch on one of the advantages offered by the Schmidt camera, which works at focal ratios of $f/2$, $f/1$ or even less. Few amateurs, however, possess such instruments, and most prefer visual to photographic equipment, or a general-purpose combination of both.

The brighter stars of clusters like the Pleiades require exposures of about one second on medium speed film in the focal plane of a 6-inch $f/8$ aluminized reflector. The brighter central region of the Orion Nebula needs only a few minutes; indeed, this part is usually grossly over-exposed in astronomical photographs, and the famous Trapezium of stars is always lost in the overall glare. 30-minute exposures of M81 and M82 (which are sufficiently close to one another to be included in the same field), will reveal their presence; but longer exposures of, say, $1\frac{1}{2}$ hours are needed to record their outer regions. Faint objects like the Crab Nebula want the same. With such objects, the length of the exposure is limited only by the stamina of the operator.

For guiding upon nebulae and clusters, the amateur must have either a long focus-guiding telescope mounted on the tube of the reflector, or else an eyepiece attached to the back of the camera. Such an eyepiece—rather like an off-centred focusing eyepiece—can be placed behind a suitable hole in the film, or, better still, set completely clear of the emulsion where it can be used to guide on star images conveniently placed at the side of the field. Great care is needed in this operation for the guide star must be accurately centred on the eyepiece cross-wires before the photographic emulsion is exposed to light, otherwise the wandering of the brighter star images will be recorded before the emulsion is correctly placed. Such an arrangement necessitates some form of mask which can be hinged or slid away from the film without introducing vibration. Guiding through the camera in this way ensures accurate registration of telescopic images upon the emulsion and compensates for slight amounts of flexure. A guiding telescope, if it is firmly mounted, and the parallelism of its axis with that of the main instrument checked before each session, is equally efficient. Cross-wires should not be too delicate if they are to be seen against the darkened field, and no form of illumination can be used in or near the field of the camera to display them; guide telescope cross-wires, on the other hand, can be illuminated. Other forms of guiding aids include image-splitting mirrors and prisms, and prismatic eyepieces placed just in front of the camera shutter. Image-splitting mirrors are usually made by half-silvering a plane-parallel glass plate so that some of the incident light is transmitted to the film and the rest reflected into an eyepiece equipped with cross-wires. For ultra-violet work the mirror could be fully silvered, but quartz must be used instead of glass.

CHAPTER 9

Light Filters

The term 'colour photography' conjures up visions of lunar and planetary pictures resplendent with all the rainbow hues. The sad fact is that very few of the heavenly bodies display any strongly-marked colours. Astronomical colours are subdued ones. When strong colours have been reported with small instruments, they have often been found due to some defect in the instrument itself. Large apertures show more colour, though this is only noticeable in the case of certain stars. Through Dr. W. H. Steavenson's 30-inch telescope, I have seen red stars that look for all the world like glowing embers. The Moon is singularly lacking in colour and it is doubtful if much would be gained by using expensive colour film.

Colour Photography

Much of the colour film sold today is expensive and processing is more complicated than that of ordinary film; not all of it can be processed by the amateur. Despite this, some readers may prefer to use this medium for their experiments. Their requirements cannot be dealt with here and they should seek advice of the film manufacturers. All the apparatus so far described can be used for colour work, since it is only in the processing that great departures from normal practice are encountered.

Paradoxically—since we are working with what might be termed 'black and white' emulsions—we can undertake colour work involving filters. Although no colours will be visible upon the finished work, the character of the photographic image will be determined by the particular transmission of the filter.

151

Filters

The filter family is a large one ranging from thin pieces of tinted gelatin to complicated and delicate optical instruments. The latter include monochromators and ingenious devices such as the famous Lyot filter.

The action of a filter is simply to transmit colours of certain wavelengths while suppressing others. Simple filters transmit broad bands of colour which are usually several hundred Ångströms wide; it is for this reason that more complicated filters have been devised, allowing narrow regions of the spectrum to be selected. Monochromators, as the name implies, were devised for this purpose.

Most pictorial photographers carry one or more filters about with them as part of their equipment. It has long been known that sky and cloud effects can be emphasized by placing a yellow filter in front of the camera lens. The reason for this is that whatever emulsion is used, it is disproportionately sensitive to the ultraviolet and blue regions of the spectrum. Thus the sky and clouds, which have more than their fair share of these wavelengths, are 'faster' photographically than terrestrial objects. Correctly exposed skies are only obtained by under-exposing the panorama below. The use of a yellow filter eliminates gross over-exposure of the area of film corresponding to the sky, and ordinary, ortho- and isochromatic emulsions can then differentiate blue sky from clouds. Panchromatic materials are able to do this without filters to some extent on account of their more balanced spectral sensitivity curves.

Yellow filters have their uses in astronomical work too. For instance, when I was photographing the crescent Venus close to the Sun, I used one to reduce the scattered shortwave radiation that is all too abundant in this region, and thereby increased the contrast between the planet and the sky. Exposures have to be a little longer, according to the density of the filter—from what we learnt in Chapter 2 we should not be surprised to hear that the density of a filter is derived from its transmission at a given wavelength.

With simple gelatin and glass filters, the colour indicates which wavelengths are transmitted best. Thus a blue filter will allow blue light to pass with negligible attenuation, while a red one will reject all colours other than red. A red postage stamp on a white envelope will completely disappear when observed through a suitable red filter.

Planetary Photography with Filters

There are so many filters—one has only to think of the names Wratten, Jena, Corning and Chance—that it is clearly impossible to deal with more than a representative few in a single chapter.

Many years ago, astronomers found that pictures of the planets taken through various coloured filters on appropriate emulsions yielded markedly different results. Photographs of Mars in blue and ultra-violet light showed more of the clouds and atmosphere of the planet, while red and infra-red emulsions and filters recorded the permanent ground markings. It is the same upon the Earth—every time the Sun sets in a clear sky, we have direct proof of the greater penetration of the longer red wavelengths than that of the shorter blue ones, the latter being scattered in the atmosphere—indeed, it has been said that the blue of our daytime sky really belongs to someone else's sunset.

When these same techniques were tried on Venus, it was expected that similar results would emerge. Rather surprisingly, infra-red and red photographs showed no markings at all—while pictures obtained with the shorter wavelengths did; and it was discovered that the further one went towards the ultra-violet, the more pronounced the markings became. Ross,[1] in 1927, obtained superb pictures of Venus in ultra-violet light, which showed considerable and rapid atmospheric movement. He used the 60-inch and 100-inch reflectors at Mt. Wilson for this programme.

Ultra-violet Photography

In the spring of 1956, Venus was a prominent evening star well

[1] Ross, F. E. *Astrophysical Journal*, Vol. 68.

placed for photography. With the active collaboration of Dr. W. H. Steavenson, I was able to take a large number of photographs of the planet,[1] some with his 30-inch and a larger number with the 6-inch reflector. Many of these were taken through an ultra-violet filter and some showed the dusky atmospheric markings.[2]

Such a programme is well suited to the amateur with a 6-inch reflector, and ultra-violet photography enables him to secure records of markings which are quite invisible to the visual observer. Ross demonstrated the difficulties of securing ultra-violet photographs before sunset—there is too much scattered light of these wavelengths while the Sun is still in the sky. This tends to reduce or even obliterate the markings on Venus, which are far from prominent at any time. He found it better to postpone ultra-violet work until after sunset. Even then, Venus must not be too low in the sky if it is to escape the effects of atmospheric absorption and turbulence. The most satisfactory time to try one's hand at this work is when the planet is at maximum elongation; it can then be photographed in a dark sky while still at a reasonable altitude.

Ultra-violet filters are made from special materials which transmit strongly in this region of the spectrum while absorbing most of the visible light. I used a Chance's OX9A filter, whose transmission is maximum at 3,600A to 3,800A and cuts off sharply just below 4,000A, close to the visual threshold. Below 3,000A the Earth's atmosphere absorbs too strongly for any useful work to be done. The astronomical photographer can use the 3,000A to 4,000A waveband if his reflecting surfaces are aluminized and he does not use glass lenses. Fluorite and quartz transmit the ultra-violet to well below the atmospheric 'cut-off'. Glass lenses can be usefully employed down to about 3,500A, excepting those made of the denser glasses. Since fluorite and quartz lenses are not generally available, the amateur, like the author, will have to work in the region between 3,500A and 4,000A; Ross used a Wratten 18A filter, whose maximum transmission is at 3,600A.

[1] Rackham, T. W. B.A.A. Journal, Vol. 67, No. 5.
[2] Moore, P. A. The Planet Venus. 1956.

A filter with optically plane surfaces may be placed in front of the eyepiece, but if the surfaces are suspect it should be fitted close to the emulsion, where small departures from flatness will have less noticeable effects. Dust and blemishes on the filter will, however, be more troublesome.

Messrs. Chance-Pilkington make several filters for ultra-violet work. The OX1 has a spectral transmission very like the OX9A. The OX7 has a better than 80% transmission between 2,900A and 3,700A; this is going considerably beyond the transmission range of glass lenses, but is ideal for quartz and fluorite lenses. The Wratten 18A is too dense for small telescopes. The OX9A suited my camera, with its positive eyepiece focusing, for it transmitted just enough visible light for the image to be focused. Also Venus could not be seen through the eyepiece until after sunset, so that by the time focusing had been completed it was possible to go straight ahead with the ultra-violet photography.

The insertion of a filter in the optical train pushes back the focal plane by one-third of the thickness of the filter and therefore destroys the focusing, if this was done without the filter. I sorted through a number of clear pieces of glass until I found one that displaced the focal plane exactly by the same amount as the interposed filter. Substituted for the filter, this allowed less brilliant objects to be focused precisely in ordinary light. With the focusing accomplished the glass was exchanged for the ultra-violet filter— without the focus being disturbed.

Most ultra-violet filters transmit some red light too—in the OX9A, the residual red, mixed with a small amount of blue, together yield purple, which is the colour of Venus as seen through the filter.

Naturally, the thickness of the glass is one factor affecting the amount of light transmitted by the filter. The OX9A was approximately one-sixteenth of an inch thick.

Before leaving the subject of ultra-violet filters, here is a word of warning. Make sure the filter transmits ultra-violet light— filters designed to absorb the ultra-violet are often advertised as ultra-violet filters. An ultra-violet transmitting filter will appear

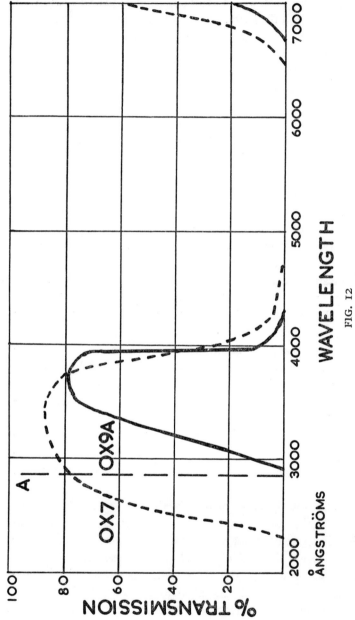

FIG. 12

Ultra-violet filter curves, by kind permission of the Chance-Pilkington Optical Works, Pilkington Bros. Ltd. A represents atmospheric 'cut-off', the lower limit for photographic work at the telescope.

almost black, and will transmit visible light only feebly—its colour should suggest blackcurrant jelly.

Infra-Red Photography

Lunar and planetary photography in the red and infra-red is well worth trying, and it is interesting to compare the highly disparate results obtained by ultra-violet and infra-red photographs obtained at the same time. Filters are available, but, in Great Britain, 35mm.

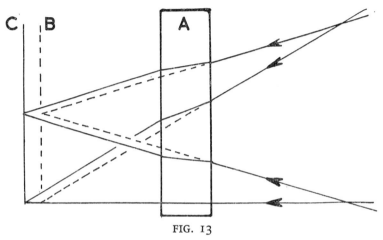

FIG. 13

The 'defocusing' effect of a glass filter

Rays of light are refracted by the plane-parallel glass filter, A, and come to a focus in the plane of C instead of B. In most cases the distance from B to C is one-third of the thickness of the filter.

film is expensive. Manufacturers will sometimes make a few feet of infra-red film to order. Storage is all-important. A refrigerator is the best place for unexposed infra-red film; it is not enough just to keep it in the dark.

It is generally easier for the amateur to use plates, either in a separate camera, or especially cut to suit the 35mm. camera. Panchromatic emulsions, while suitable for the visible red, are not sensitive to infra-red. Infra-red sensitive 35mm. film is sold by Gavaerts and Eastman Kodak.

It is important to note that, while a reflecting telescope mirror is perfectly achromatic and will reflect light rays of widely differing wavelengths to the same Newtonian focal plane, the insertion of an enlarging eyepiece in the optical train, besides increasing the effective focal length, will destroy the achromatism. No enlarging eyepiece will be achromatic in the infra-red and, as camera focusing cannot be carried out visually, the best infra-red effective focal plane must be found empirically by making several photographic exposures and by racking out and noting the setting of the camera attachment for each one of them. Regarding the determination of a reflecting telescope's infra-red effective focal plane, it is best to forget the film manufacturers' advice which advocates the setting back of the emulsion from the camera lens by an additional $1/400$ part of the visual emulsion-to-lens focusing distance. This rule is for short focus cameras and might serve as a useful basis for finding the infra-red effective focal length of a refractor, but if it is applied to reflectors working at very great effective focal lengths, such as are used for lunar and planetary work, the deduced distances to be added will be very much in excess of the correct ones. Generally the infra-red focal plane will be no more than a millimetre or two behind that of the visual and some of this displacement will be due to refraction in the infra-red filter—Cassegrain telescope photographers please note.

Other Useful Filters

Town-dwelling telescope owners often suffer from the effects of street lighting. Ordinary tungsten lamps have to be endured, but the odium of sodium can be to a large extent mitigated by using didymium and neodymium filters. These absorb the yellow wavelengths very efficiently, while transmitting the rest of the visible spectrum. The effect to the naked eye is almost magical and photography under these difficult conditions will be much improved at the cost of having to make slightly longer exposures.

Other available filters have maximum transmissions in the green, minimum in the red, reasonable transmissions in the infra-red but none in the ultra-violet. On account of the resemblance of this spectral distribution (apart from the infra-red) to that of the human eye, these are sometimes known as ortho- or isochromatic filters. Photographers with refracting telescopes are well advised to employ such filters in the optical train—otherwise, the blue-violet end of the spectrum will dominate the longer wavelengths, and if the focus has been determined by eye the blue-violet images will be out of focus. The use of the filter, with orthochromatic emulsions, enables the celestial body to be photographed in the same colour as is used for the focusing.

Heat-absorbing Filters etc.

Other filters transmit well in the visible region but absorb the infra-red. These are called heat-absorbing filters and may be beneficially employed for solar work. Neutral filters transmit a known proportion of the complete visible spectrum, but are considerably more transparent to the infra-red. A good combination for solar work would be a heat-absorbing filter followed by a neutral one nearer the camera. Between them they would absorb most of the visible and infra-red wavelengths.

What happens to the heat in a heat-absorbing filter? Since it goes in one side and does not emerge from the other, the answer is simple—the filter gets hot. A considerable temperature gradient may be set up across a thick filter, the hot side expanding while the cooler side tends to resist this expansion. Excessive heating will shatter the glass. Much depends upon the size of the Sun's image striking the filter, since a large, unfocused image will spread the same amount of heat over a wider area of the filter.

With front surface metal-on-glass filters heat is not absorbed, but is reflected harmlessly away.

Effects of Filters on Exposure

The insertion of a filter into the optical train naturally reduces the amount of light reaching the photographic emulsion. Exposures must therefore be extended. This is not as straightforward as might appear at first glance. Not only must the spectral distributions of both filter and emulsion be considered, but there is also the spectral distribution of the light from the celestial body itself to be taken into account. A filter designed to transmit the yellow light from Jupiter will obviously be less efficient in transmitting the predominantly red light of Mars. It would, in fact, have a different exposure factor in the two cases; the factor for Mars would be numerically the higher, indicating the necessity of longer exposures.

Data concerning filters can always be obtained from the manufacturers. The exposure factor of a filter whose maker is not known can be found by trial and error: a series of varied exposures (carefully noted) will provide all the information that is required.

Ultra-violet filters are deceptive—usually the filter factor turns out to be less than would be expected, since the filter can 'see' in a region where the observer is blind. During the 1956 Venus apparition I found that the Chance OX9A filter had a factor of 10 with panchromatic film: whereas unfiltered photographs were sufficiently exposed in 1/10 second, ultra-violet shots required 1 second.

Darkroom Filters

Filters also form part of the darkroom equipment—safelight glasses are no more than filters designed to absorb the dangerously actinic short-wave region of the spectrum. Green safelights for the slower panchromatic emulsions are, in my opinion, worthless—the light from them is too dim. Since faster panchromatic emulsions have to be processed in complete darkness, there is no hardship in dealing similarly with the slower ones. Light-brown safelight screens are intended for bromide enlarging papers and other slow non-colour materials. Dark red screens are for orthochromatic work, and orange ones enable the processing of very slow non-colour materials, such as contact papers, document papers and the like. Infra-red plates and film can be processed in yellow-green

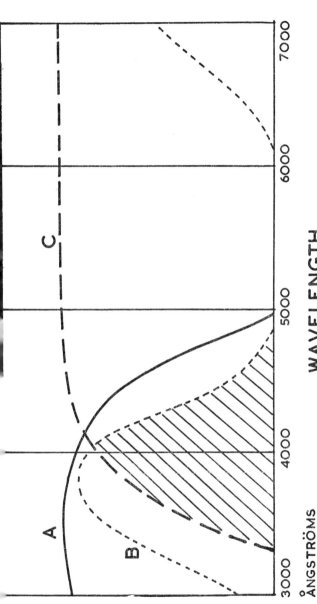

ÅNGSTRÖMS

WAVELENGTH

FIG. 14

Curve A represents the spectral response of a blue-sensitive emulsion, B is the transmission curve of a glass filter, C the transmission of a glass lens in the optical train. C limits B and together they impose further limitations upon the emulsion, resulting in loss of speed and bandwidth. Above 6000A both B and C transmit, but the emulsion is 'blind' to these wavelengths. The shaded portion is all that is recorded by the emulsion.

illumination, although it is better to tank-develop 35mm. infra-red film in the same way as ordinary 35mm. film.

If the amateur wishes to purchase a single safelight screen for general use—other than for panchromatic and infra-red processing—he should choose a red one.

A plane parallel red filter hinged to intercept the light emerging from the enlarger facilitates the accurate placing of the sensitive paper below, which will not be affected by the red image falling on it.

CHAPTER 10

Developing and Processing

After loading the camera in complete darkness and exposing the film at the telescope we must render the latent images visible by development. Impatience to see the results of the work of the telescope has ruined many good negatives in the past, so the amateur would be well-advised to address himself to the task in an unhurried and methodical manner. If he wants to lose a lot of fun he can take his film to a professional processing establishment, but he must warn them of what to expect.

Methods

There are two developing techniques—tank and dish. For the amateur with 35mm. film, there is nothing better than time-and-temperature tank development. Tanks are also procurable for plates, particularly for panchromatic emulsions which would otherwise have to be processed in complete darkness. Ortho- and blue-sensitive plates can be dish developed under an orange or red safelight, which allows the worker to see what is happening to them and, if necessary, to terminate development at any time; time, and the temperature of solutions, are therefore not important.

Spiral Tanks

Spiral developing tanks for film are well established these days. In earlier models, the film was pushed into the end of the groove and the loading was continued by hand until all the film was safely in—unless it jammed half-way. Quite often jamming did occur—and a vexatious business it was, in complete darkness.

163

Modern spiral tanks incorporate some device to obviate this difficulty. The trimmed end of the film is inserted an inch or two into the groove when it can be felt to contact the loading mechanism; the film is then fed into the tank by rotating one of the grooved film holders backwards and forwards.

Sometimes in the old-type spirals, the film could be loaded as far as the last few inches. I found that, rather than remove it and start again—it is always unwise to handle film more than necessary —these last few recalcitrant inches could be got in by submerging the whole film holder in water in the tank. With a clockwise spiral, viewed from the top, a few sharp clockwise rotations of the complete spiral would jerk the whole of the film into the groove. Likewise, sharp anti-clockwise motions will sometimes unload the grooves and may damage the film. Film purchased in bulk must be cut to suitable lengths for both the camera spools and the developing tank. There are two sorts of tank in current use: those taking the standard 1·6 m. or 5 ft. reloads for 36 exposures, and the smaller ones designed for twenty frames of colour film. The latter have transparent spirals.

Having loaded the tank with film, it is important that the light-tight lid should be immediately and firmly seated on top. Do not allow bright light to fall perpendicularly upon the tank: it might enter the filling hole in the centre and somehow get to the film. I have never had any trouble in this respect, and I have not sought to invite it.

When panchromatic film is used, the tank, like the camera, must be loaded in total darkness. Failing a proper darkroom, a cupboard can be adapted for this purpose; even a well-curtained room after dark can be safely used; but ideally, the darkroom should have running water and a reasonable-sized sink. Light-tight cloth bags large enough to hold all the necessary impedimenta as well as the operator's hands, are available commercially. These can be used in bright lights—but if darker corners exist nearby, why tempt providence?

In this connection, I have heard of the tyro who used a tea-pot for a tank and loaded this with his head and shoulders under the bed covers. Such methods are not conducive to fine work, despite their ingenuity.

Once the tank is loaded and sealed against light, all the subsequent processing operations can be performed in natural or artificial light.

Developing Equipment

For developing, the astronomical photographer will need the following:

(1) A glass thermometer. This need not have a long range since film is normally processed within a few degrees of 68° F., or 20° C.

(2) A measuring cylinder or beaker calibrated in fluid ounces or cubic centimetres. 20 fluid ounces or 500 c.c. is large enough.

(3) One medium-sized polythene funnel—glass will do, but the others bounce.

(4) Several glass bottles with well-fitting ground glass or rubber stoppers. One for developer, one for acid fixer and hardener; others for general storage.

(5) A mixing vessel with a capacity of about 35 fluid ounces or 1 litre. A pyrex flask, or any other low-expansion glass container with thin walls can be used. Sometimes, during cold weather, solutions must be warmed before use.

(6) Clock. Some sort of reliable timepiece. The Smith 'Pinger', which rings a bell after a pre-set interval has elapsed, is useful but not essential.

The Developing Process

Developing and fixing solutions can be bought almost ready for use, but despite this the worker may prefer to mix his own ingredients. Personally, I find astronomical photography sufficiently time-consuming without this additional chore.

At this point we are dealing more with methods than chemicals, so we can leave the actual choice of these until later. My own *modus operandi* is summarized below; it probably differs in detail from that of other workers.

The developing tank, the reader will remember, is loaded and ready for the processing of the film.

(1) First determine the room temperature; if it is less than about 17° C., the tank, solutions, etc., will have to be warmed.

(2) Measure off the amount of developer and water sufficient to fill the tank; this amount is usually stated on the lid of the tank. When diluting developers, note that a dilution of 3:1 involves *four* volumes—do not pour in one volume and top it up to three, as this will be a 2:1 dilution and a good deal 'faster' than the intended one.

(3) Warm some water, mix it with cold until the temperature is about 21° C., add a drop or two of wetting agent—the effect of this liquid is out of all proportion to its small volume, and too much may cause the water to froth. Pour the warmed water plus wetting agent into the developing tank until it is full to overflowing. The tank can be placed in a photographic dish to collect what spills over. Agitate vigorously for about a quarter of a minute. Leave for a few minutes. The reason for this initial rinse is two-fold:

   a. To bring the tank and film to the required temperature.
   b. To make sure that the film is uniformly wet and to eliminate air-bubbles, which will cause blank spots on the negatives and black ones on the prints.

(4) During the few minutes the tank and film are being warmed, the developer in the thin glass mixing vessel can also be warmed. The quickest way is over an electrical heater, hot-plate, gas-ring or whatever happens to be available. Excessive heat should be avoided and the solution must be kept moving by gentle shaking. The temperature should be checked at frequent intervals, and the heating stopped when it approaches 21° C. (70° F.).

An alternative method involves a bowl of warm water. Its temperature should be fairly high—about 40° C. (100° F.), or the thin glass container and developer, when immersed in it, will not reach 20° C. (68° F.) in a reasonable time.

166

During hot weather, solutions that are too warm can easily be cooled by running tap water over the containers. The temperature of tap water seldom approaches 20° C.—earth makes a fine insulator for metal water pipes buried well below the surface.

(5) Empty away the warm water and wetting agent from the tank. Pour in the developer and agitate well for a few seconds. Start the clock or 'Pinger', or note the time developing should end; better still, jot it down on a pad. Agitate backwards and for-wards and up and down for a few seconds in each minute during development. Agitation of the solutions plays a prominent part in developing and some attempt should be made to standardize the method.

(6) During the odd periods between spells of agitation, the acid fixer and hardener can be warmed in the same mixing vessel as was used for the developer.

(7) Development completed, as indicated by the clock, pour off the solution into a storage bottle. Immediately fill the tank with fixer, and agitate. It is not necessary to note the time. After about three minutes the lid can be removed and the tank and its contents should then be left to cool down.

Some workers favour immersing the film in a stop bath before fixing. In my opinion, this is just another solution to warm up—it is unwise to plunge film into solutions of widely different temperatures—and a fresh acid hypo and hardener solution should do all that is required. The acid content is important, for this 'kills' any remaining traces of developer.

(8) Fixing should be complete in about five minutes. Pour off the solution into another storage bottle. Place the tank, minus its lid, under the cold water tap and allow the film to wash for about 30 minutes. It is worth emphasizing again that warm film should never be placed in very cold water, as the sudden transition may damage the emulsion.

(9) A final rinse in water containing a few drops of wetting agent will promote even and quicker drying. To the uninitiated, the addition of wetting agents to assist drying usually comes as a

167

surprise. One of the main functions of a wetting agent is to break down surface tension: without it, the water on the drying film will form into droplets which will dry much slower than the rest of the film. The gelatin under these droplets is maintained in a more swollen state than that which has already dried and, furthermore, when these droplets finally dry out, they very often leave marks on the film caused by sediment suspended in the water.

Quick drying offers less scope to the 'dust-bug'.

Final words about drying. Do not handle film more than is required. Do not sponge it down. Despite what others say, do not try to accelerate drying with fans, etc.—the danger from dust is too great. Hang the film up; bulldog clips, croc clips and sprung clothes pegs are suitable. A clothes peg clipped on to the lower end provides enough weight to keep the film straight. Leave the film for several hours in a quiet, non-turbulent atmosphere. Do not attempt to print or enlarge from it until it is absolutely dry. Haste and fuss do not pay off—patience and persistence do.

Plate Development

The processing of plates follows a parallel course to that of film. The initial rinse with wetting agent and water is most important, but for dish development it is perhaps better to forgo this in preference to adding a few drops of the wetting agent to the developer. When introducing plates to the solutions, immerse them quickly and uniformly. This is more easily promoted by adding a little wetting agent—only a few drops, or frothing will result and this may make it difficult to watch the progress of development (assuming it is not a panchromatic plate, which must of course be developed in a light-tight tank by the time-and-temperature method).

When the processing has been completed, the plate is washed. The stream of water from the tap should not be allowed to fall directly on it; rather, a flow of running water should be maintained across it, followed by a final rinse containing wetting agent. On account of the suspended particles in tap water, some workers rightly advocate a final rinse in distilled water plus wetting agent.

Drying is carried out in drying racks which should be located in dust-free containers. It is always unwise to try and accelerate this process.

At least two dishes are necessary for dish development, one for developer and the other for fixer. After development, the plate must be removed from one dish to the other. Bare fingers should never be immersed in developing solutions: some of the chemicals —particularly Metol, which is disguised under several trade names —cause distressing skin conditions. People so affected should use non-metol developers. The plate can be supported in an easily-contrived metal or plastic clip, or holder, with the handle above the surface of the solutions. Stainless steel and nickel are suitable metals, perspex and celluloid are recommended plastics, but even a humble piece of tinned copper wire can be fashioned into such a device.

Plates in metal developing tanks are submitted to the same developing ritual as film in the spiral tanks, and there is no need to recapitulate. One or two points have to be watched: for example, a tank may be difficult to fill with solution—often this can be remedied by slackening off the lid slightly, without introducing light into the tank; this also facilitates emptying, which should always be as rapid as possible.

Fine-Grain Development

All plates and films must be processed in fine-grain developers if we are to approach maximum resolution. It is worthwhile to discuss the basic ideas behind fine-grain development. To do this, we must first consider the emulsion and its structure.

We learnt in Chapter 2 that all emulsions contain tiny silver halide grains. These are quite invisible to the eye, being of the order of one-thousandth of a millimetre across. If the performance of an emulsion depended upon these only, there would be no difficulty whatsoever. Unfortunately, during the developing processes, changes occur which cause the individual grains to coalesce into larger and coarser conglomerations, each containing a large number of the original particles. The emulsion thus exhibits an irregular and blotchy texture, and it is on this that the developed image is superimposed. These irregularities must not be confused with image detail—they are merely the bricks of which it is composed. Graininess is the name given to these larger conglomerations. It is this and not the original grain size, before development, that limits the degree of permissible enlargement for a given emulsion.

The function of fine-grain developers, as the name implies, is to prevent the growth of these larger grainy communities. There are at least four distinct ways of achieving this, but three of them have serious disadvantages. Developers containing p-phenylene-diamine provide the yardstick in fine-grain developing. For some obscure reason, no other developing agent produces such fine graininess in an emulsion. From the practical viewpoint, these advantages are more than offset by the greatly reduced emulsion speed and the toxic effects upon the user.

Another way is to develop the emulsion to a very low value of γ. This can be done either by diluting the developer or by reducing the time of development. To appreciate this, it must be remembered that as the halide grains are reduced to metallic silver they grow in size, and as they do so, they may bridge the gaps separating them. Thus a number of discrete particles can soon form a comparatively large piece of metallic silver. By limiting the strength or time of development, the reduction can cease before the 'bridging over' becomes serious. Loss of emulsion speed and contrast are serious disadvantages of this method.

Physical development is a process whereby the photo-sensitized silver halide grains are coated with metallic silver from the developer. Again, fine grain is only achieved at the expense of emulsion speed.

Lastly there are the so-called solvent developers. In addition to the reducing agent itself (which changes, by the release of the halogen base, the halide grains to metallic silver) these contain a silver halide solvent. The task of this chemical is to dissolve or eat away the outer region of the silver halide grains as development proceeds. Thus, when the halide has been reduced to silver, the grains will not be so large and there will be less 'bridging over'. True, there is some attendant loss of emulsion speed, for some of the exposed halide will inevitably be dissolved before it can be developed. Nevertheless, these developers have enjoyed a well-deserved popularity for many years.

When printing and enlarging there is no point in using fine grain developers; bottles of neat 'universal' type developers are readily available for this work. These can easily be diluted to the correct working proportions according to the makers' recommendations.

When processing negative materials, close watch should be kept upon temperature—a degree or so either way will make very appreciable differences in developing times. Solutions work more slowly at lower temperatures—below about 15° C. (60° F.) they sometimes refuse to work at all.

In astronomical work it is important to err, if at all, on the side of under-exposure and under-development. Work to gamma of 0·7 rather than 0·8 when calculating development times. Over-exposure leads to more scattered light in the emulsion, which reduces resolution and contrast. Over-development produces larger clumps of grain, reduced contrast, and possibly chemical fog. Fog due to over-development spreads over the whole film—even to unexposed areas. Fog due to over-exposure is limited to the particular frame which was over-exposed.

Fixing Solutions

There is little point in repeating information already given in Chapter 2 concerning fixing solutions. These can be made up and stored for months if necessary. When they show indisputable signs of slowing down, they should be discarded: discard a fixing solution which at normal temperatures is unable to clear an emulsion in about 3–4 minutes. Until the emulsion is cleared it will appear milky—fixing should proceed for about twice the time that the solution takes to clear the plate or film. It is difficult to make hard-and-fast rules about fixing solutions; when there is any doubt about the age or efficiency of a solution (and this applies not only to fixers) throw it away and prepare a new one.

The Ideal Negative

Having exposed, developed, fixed, washed and dried the emulsion, we are now able to examine the results of our labours. What should the ideal negative look like? Here there is no unanimity of opinion.

My idea of a good lunar negative is one that is neither too light nor too dense: there should be no 'clogging up' with metallic silver of those parts that correspond to the highlights of the finished print. Too dense a negative is the result of either over-exposure or over-development, or both. Weak negatives result from under-exposure and under-development. Under-exposure with correct development will show only the brighter areas of the subject, while correct exposure and under-development yield weak images of all parts of the subject. The clear parts of a negative should be transparent and free of fog (the latter being the product of several factors—over-exposure, over-development, stray light, old film and processing at too high a temperature). Under certain conditions of lighting (viewed under a bright light against a dark background) a negative that is too thin can be made to appear like a positive.

Best results are obtained when all the densities are recorded along the straight portion of the emulsion's characteristic curve. The shoulder, representing over-exposure, should be avoided. With faint objects, the light-grasp of the telescope may be inadequate to avoid the toe of the curve, and densities will be recorded in a non-linear manner.

Planetary images, like lunar ones, should appear on the negative without opaque blacks. The size of over-exposed planetary images is exaggerated, owing to halation and general light scatter; if haloes appear round them, they are grossly over-exposed. Distorted images—the crescent Venus shaped like a boomerang, for example —are the result of atmospheric turbulence, as is all-over fuzziness.

Guided star images should record on the negative as tiny, dense, round discs. Not much can be done about the brighter star images, as opposed to those of the fainter ones. Some are bound to be over-exposed, some just right, while others will be too faint. They will, in fact, be registered along the whole length of the gamma or characteristic curve of the film. Over-exposed images will almost certainly have appendages of some sort, such as diffraction patterns from the diagonal supports, as well as some halation. Such star images look as though they would be more at home on a Christmas card.

Whole-disc solar images should also be free of halation; over-exposure also tends to minimize contrast between sunspots and the photosphere. It must always be borne in mind that with slower emulsions we have not as much exposure latitude as with fast, so that to achieve the best results our exposures must be carefully timed—otherwise, we may easily run off the straight part of the steep characteristic curve.

Post-development treatment of Negatives

What can be done if our negatives are found to be too light or too dense? Is there any post-development treatment that will cure these defects? The answer is—up to a point, yes. The process known as intensification will 'fatten up' thin negatives—provided only that there is *some* metallic silver for the intensifier to work on. Something more than a smile must be present on an emulsion before it can be intensified to reveal a Cheshire cat.

Processing is easy, and can be carried out in daylight or artificial light. Whatever is done to the film after fixing can be done in bright light, for the film will never be light-sensitive again. One method is to bleach the film in a special bath until the denser parts are a light silvery-grey. It is extremely important to remove all traces of hypo from the film first, to prevent staining. After the bleach, the film can be placed in one of several solutions, developers included, and darkening will occur—and to a greater degree than before. The whole process can be repeated if the first intensification is insufficient. But one point must be watched carefully— graininess is increased each time.

The reverse process is that of reduction, which removes metallic silver from areas of the emulsion that are too dense, and cleans up the fog from the lighter parts. For our type of work, where contrast is usually welcome, subtractive reducers are best. Perhaps the most famous is Farmer's reducer, which reduces all densities equally. Thus a larger proportion of metallic silver is removed from the lighter areas than the darker ones and this leads to greater contrast. There is a corresponding reduction in graininess.

The emulsion must be carefully washed and dried after both treatments.

It should be emphasized that these treatments are, at the best, only 'get-outs' to save inferior negatives, and the results will never equal a correctly-exposed negative. The aim of the astronomical photographer must be to gauge his exposures and to process his film so that intensification and reduction will be unnecessary.

Storing Solutions

There is no need to discard photographic solutions after one spell of processing. They can be stored in stoppered bottles, kept in a cool, dark place; they must of course be labelled. A row of unlabelled bottles is a depressing sight and it is not always easy to determine their contents. Fixing hypo has a characteristic scent, but developers cannot always be picked out by this method.

Before solutions are used again for further processing, they should always be filtered. Filter papers placed in glass or polythene funnels are too slow without a vacuum pump. Some workers use wads of cotton wool and submit their precious emulsions to hazards arising from the presence of linty fibres. I have found that a piece of fine-weave parachute nylon works quickly and well, and is inert to most photographic chemicals. Tapwater containing suspended particles can be filtered simply by attaching a nylon bag to the spout with an elastic band.

Storing Emulsions

Lastly, film storage. Film must be kept flat and paper albums are sold for this express purpose. Better still, buy a few sheets of grease-proof paper and make them for yourself. Do *not* store film rolled up—at the slightest provocation, the middle will shoot out to produce a 'magic wand', and scratched negatives will be the result. Furthermore a length of rolled film is a most intractable object, tending to roll up like the comic waiter's shirt-front, if given half a chance.

CHAPTER 11

The Darkroom and its Equipment

D arkrooms—it is indeed difficult to find anything original to say about them, for the literature already devoted to them is copious.

So far, throughout this book, we have managed to get along with scarcely a mention of the darkroom. Dark corners and curtained rooms have satisfied our needs, and film has been tank developed and processed without its help. Now we have to face the fact that we cannot make further progress unless we have some form of darkroom in which to do our printing and enlarging.

A spare cellar, attic or loft offers immediate scope for conversion—if it happens to be available. Bathrooms are often pressed into temporary service—their unlimited water supplies being the chief attraction. Large cupboards, other than the dusty one under the stairs, also have possibilities. Sheds are not good—apart from dustiness, they generally suffer formidable changes in temperature.

If absolutely no accommodation can be arranged within his dwelling, the amateur must look further afield. For example, he may be able to team up with another enthusiast who *does* own a darkroom. Or again, he might join a local camera club and share the facilities of the communal darkroom.

But a privately-owned darkroom is undoubtedly to be preferred. It need not be lavishly fitted out, and a good deal of the equipment can be made by the amateur himself.

Light Exclusion

The first requirement is complete darkness. Windows must be covered with some opaque material, and there is no reason why this should not be permanently fixed. The window of my dark-room is covered by a hardboard shutter which fits snugly against the window frame and is held in place by springy, flat, metal clips. Ventilation—an important consideration—is provided by a series of fairly large holes near the top of the shutter. A sheet of hard-board on either side of these, separated from the shutter itself by pieces of inch-thick wood on three sides only, completes the light trap. Thus the air has to describe a hair-pin-shaped path through the shutter. Darkroom ventilating fans, complete with light-traps, are expensive, and the amateur would be well advised to consider his other darkroom requirements first. As for light-tight entrances—do not worry about them; just lock the door.

Darkroom Furniture

A water supply and a sink or sinks are not really luxuries. A good deal of work *can* be done without running water, but great benefits are bestowed on the worker who has running water in his darkroom. I have had experience of both. If hot running water is also available, so much the better.

The layout of the darkroom must be dictated by its shape and size. There is no right and wrong way of arranging things, the sole criterion being convenience, and this must be left to the in-dividual.

The essential items of darkroom equipment are listed below:

(1) First, an enlarger. This may be either home-made or pur-chased. If it is to be used exclusively for 35mm. film, it should be capable of a magnification of at least 10. Models for larger plates or films employ lenses of longer focal length to maintain un-distorted coverage of the frame size, and are not able to produce such high magnifications. Many modern enlargers are auto-matically focused when they are raised and lowered—this *is* a luxury. Quite a few of them are unsteady, particularly near the top of the supporting column which is just the wrong place for un-steadiness—at the point of maximum magnification. The column of my enlarger is firmly bracketed to the wall at both ends.

(2) A table under the enlarger. This should be rock-steady and large enough to supply a reasonable working area for masking frames and other equipment used during the work.

(3) A bench or table—or, better still, a lead-lined tray with one end opening into the sink. Its purpose is to support the 'wet' apparatus—the developing dishes, tanks, bottles, etc. during processing. Unwanted liquids can also be swabbed down the sink. Wood batten frames are often set in the metal tray to assist drainage. The worker is advised to build his sink at an adequate distance from the enlarging table: hypo is only one of several chemicals which can be a nuisance if they manage to get on to the photographic papers before they should.

(4) Safelights are important and indispensable items. There are lots of different makes; the one I use is a plastic Paterson, with interchangeable red and orange screw-on covers. Whatever safelight is chosen, respect the maker's recommendations regarding wattage of lamp and distance from work, and check on its suitability for the emulsions to be used. In connection with darkroom illumination, it may be said that the days of blackwalled darkrooms are over, and these 'dungeons' have given way to comparatively bright and cheerful rooms, with light-toned walls. As long as the 'safe' light *is* safe, no harm is done if it is reflected about the room from the walls. Recommended wall colour—cream. All electrical installations must be beyond suspicion; if in doubt, consult an expert.

(5) Thermometers, measuring and mixing vessels, storage bottles etc., belong to the tank developing equipment; this was described in the last chapter, and need not be recapitulated.

(6) Masking frames are used on the enlarging table. Their function is threefold. First, to hold the enlarging papers flat—some tend to turn up at the corners. Secondly, to provide white surrounds to the enlargements. Thirdly, to enable each successive piece of enlarging paper to be exactly located with reference to the enlarger.

Not much work is involved in making adjustable masking frames. All sorts of bits and pieces lend themselves to their construction. The basic type consists of a largish plywood baseboard, one hinged L-shaped but otherwise non-adjustable member which supplies two sides of a rectangular frame, and two straight blades clamped or clipped to it. The size of the mask is adjustable down to the inside corner of the L-piece.

'Solid'-type masking frames, like wide picture frames, can be cut from any suitable material—hardboard does very well—the aperture being governed by the paper size.

A flat glass plate is sometimes used to hold down the sheet of enlarging paper. It must be clean and free from dust, smudges, fingerprints, and bubbles or other flaws in the glass.

(7) A range of photographic dishes for small, medium and large papers; the smaller ones are also useful for plate development. Using the right-sized dish is economical of developing solutions.

Two pairs of photographic tweezers—one for developer, the other for fixer. If they are identical, wind a piece of coloured plastic tape around one of them where it will show clearly without getting in the way. If the developer tweezers are inadvertently plunged in the fixer (or vice versa), wash them immediately.

(8) Print dryers. I cannot make up my mind if these are unnecessary luxuries or not. If the prints have to be glazed (on no account use 'art' papers with fancy surfaces) a dryer is a very definite 'must'. I use a home-made one made from a large and ancient government-surplus radio chassis. This rectangular chassis houses electric heaters under a gently curving sheet of aluminium. The prints are placed either on this or a highly-polished metal sheet lying on the aluminium shield. The prints are maintained in intimate contact with the metal by means of a linen cloth stretched over them. After a few minutes, the enlargements come crackling off dry—and if from the glazing plate, glossy too. Even distribution of the heat is essential.

(9) Enlarging exposure times range from a second or two, for a small degree of enlargement, to several minutes if large pictures are needed from fairly dense negatives. Some form of time-piece must therefore be used for this work. Anything which will break up a minute into its sixty equal parts will do. A stop clock or watch is more convenient to use than, say, an electric clock with a

second hand: the latter is continuously moving, while the former can be set to zero at the beginning of each exposure. Electronic timers which switch off the enlarger at the end of a pre-set time interval are very useful when many enlargements are required from the same negative.

I have converted what is advertised as a 'contactor time switch' into a darkroom clock. It is an extremely robust government-surplus clockwork movement designed to give two electrical impulses per second. They can still be obtained for less than one pound, and are a very good buy. The movement is wound up in the usual way by a knob, which unwinds at the rate of one rotation per 30 minutes. A large circular scale of metal, cardboard or any other material is easily fitted to the metal case of the movement and a pointer attached to the winding spindle. The scale is divided into thirty minutes and each of these into quarters. From the 30-minute mark, which is also the zero mark, a pin projects as a stop for the pointer. During operations, the clock is started and left running—it is the pointer which, being only clipped to the central winding spindle, can quickly and easily be reset at zero at the beginning of each exposure. For tank development a croc clip can be set at the appropriate position on the time scale, and when the pointer reaches it the developing process is stopped. Being divided into minutes and quarters of a minute, the scale can be read with sufficient accuracy to about 5 seconds, which is enough for most of our work. Shorter exposures can be timed by counting the 'ticks' at the rate of four per second.

(10) Guillotines for trimming the prints and enlargements save much work, and although they can be bought, not much skill is needed in their construction. Designs vary, but all consist basically of a fixed blade against which slides a movable one. Anything inserted between them—fingers included—is submitted to a shearing, scissor-like action. Hardened blades, while desirable, are by no means essential. Efficient blades can be made from two pieces of $1\frac{1}{2} \times \frac{1}{8}$ inch mild steel strip. These are placed together and drilled at one end to take a $\frac{1}{4}$-inch pivoting screw, with spring washers and locking nuts. The fixed blade is drilled and counter-

sunk to take the heads of the woodscrews that hold it to the edge of a thick wooden base-board; these are then well clear of the movable blade. The print to be trimmed is firmly held upon the base-board so that the edge overhangs the fixed blade. The knife is then pulled down towards the operator; this action—rather like that of 'pulling a pint'—trims the print cleanly. During this process it is as well to press the moveable blade laterally towards the fixed one. Sometimes there is a tendency to fold rather than to cut the print, owing to the blades parting slightly. When blunt, they can be sharpened with a file; their cutting edges should be square—not tapered like knife-blades. The length of the cutting edges should be an inch or two greater than the maximum length of paper that will have to be cut.

Other appurtenances of the darkroom (mainly small items) include 'squeegee' rollers, print washers, plastic stirring rods, scissors, enlarger film holders, enlarger focusing devices, fine dusting brushes, a magnifying glass etc.

The impecunious amateur who thumbs through the manufacturers' catalogues will find all sorts of expensive photographic apparatus, embodying the latest refinements. He should not be discouraged by this display of equipment that he cannot afford: most of it is unnecessarily luxurious, and equally good results can be obtained, less conveniently, with much simpler apparatus.

CHAPTER 12

Enlarging Techniques

W e will suppose that somehow or other a darkroom has been found and equipped, and film has been exposed and developed to produce negatives; at last the way is clear for the final operation of all—that of making positives by enlargement. Printing processes are only mentioned in passing, for, almost without exception, all our negatives are too small to make contact prints.

Since the emphasis throughout this book has been on 35mm. work, the enlarging process will be described with this in view, All enlargers, regardless of size and shape, horizontal or vertical. work in essentially the same way.

Before dealing with the sequence of enlarging operations, it would perhaps be advisable to take a closer look at the enlarger itself. Ignoring the column and other parts of the mounting, there are four principal components:

(1) The lamp housing, a metal box containing an opal lamp—a wattage of 100 to 150 is high enough for most work. Light-trapped ventilation is necessary with these lamps.

(2) The condenser lens assembly, consisting of one or two plano-convex lenses of wide aperture and very short focal length. With two, the lenses are mounted with their convex surfaces nearly in contact. The function of condensing lenses is to distribute the light from the lamp evenly over an area rather greater than that of the negative to be enlarged. The latter, in its holder, is placed close to the lower, plane surface of the condenser lens assembly.

If for some reason illumination is not uniform, the enlargements will be ruined. A degree of uneven illumination which may be tolerable to the eye will produce intolerable intensity gradients on the enlarging paper emulsion—particularly on a contrasty one.

Some enlargers are fitted with diffusing screens instead of condensers, but these are not suited to our type of work, since they suffer from the serious drawback of reducing contrast.

(3) The enlarging bellows are traditionally made from thin leather and are similar to camera bellows. This arrangement, complete with rigid carriage and focusing knob, is still in common use, though to some extent it has been superseded by 'helical focusing': instead of bellows, coarse-threaded metal cylinders are so made that one, with the lens fitted to the lower end, can be adjusted within the other by rotating it.

A narrow slot, wide enough to contain the film-holder, separates the lamp housing and condenser lens assembly from the lower portion, which consists of the bellows, projector lens and associated parts.

(4) The quality of the projector lens of an enlarger is proportional to the depth of the purchaser's pocket. It is false economy to buy a cheap and inferior one—far better to buy an old camera and use the lens from that.

Any lens which projects a pincushion- or barrel-shaped image of a square aperture is useless. An aperture of $f/6 \cdot 3$ is sufficient for all our needs—most workers using larger apertures stop down, in any case. An iris diaphragm, while convenient, is not essential.

Home constructors can make enlargers out of old, bellows-type cameras with a few odds and ends and a little ingenuity. Enlarging lenses are made for short distance work and differ in this respect from camera lenses computed for infinity. With shorter focal length camera lenses, such as we need to provide the considerable enlargement required with 35mm. negatives, the differences are slight, and a good camera lens is certainly not to be despised. My own home-made enlarger incorporates an $f/6 \cdot 3$ Wray enlarging anastigmat. Any lens that reduces the image definition already provided by the telescope must be put on one side for less exacting work.

In setting up the enlarger, the worker must be quite certain the planes of the film holder, enlarging lens and masking frame (*i.e.*, table top) are parallel. Condenser lenses must be free of dust and blemishes; the most important lens surface is that nearest the film-holder. Should the lenses be of poor quality, as is often the case, the better one should be placed next to the film. Two grades of condenser lenses are sold: the moulded inexpensive ones and the optically worked superior type.

Film-Holders

Holders for miniature film are designed to keep the film flat during enlarging. Although constructional details vary, they fall into two distinct categories—the glass and the glassless. The former is the older and the more troublesome, being no more than a 'sandwich' consisting of two glass plates, with the film as the 'meat' between them. Some sort of clip or similar device facilitates the 'sandwiching'. No doubt the film is held flat by this method, but this scarcely compensates for its drawbacks. Glass surfaces are easily smeared, and easily collect dust. The surfaces in contact with the film must be cleaned each time a negative is changed since any dust here will be in focus on the surface of the printing paper; it may well damage the negative too. Moreover, despite the 'sandwiching', only relatively small areas of the film come into really close contact with the glass surfaces. Other regions will exhibit interference patterns or Newton's fringes; these may be interesting physical phenomena but they are no friends of the photographer when he detects them on his finished enlargements.

Glass film holders are more useful with larger films and it is almost impossible to keep these flat any other way; also, the degree of enlargement is seldom as great, so that dust hazards are reduced.

Glassless film holders retain the 'sandwich' idea but only at the edges. All the metal above and below the area of the film frame is removed, and light from the lamp passes only through the negative on its way to the projecting lens below. Clips attached to the all-metal film-holder, not only hold the 'sandwich' together, but supply pressure around the edges of the film which helps to resist movement due to thermal effects of the lamp. Sometimes these are sufficient to distort the film and defocus the enlarger, and, unless they are watched, can cause more trouble than inferior enlarging lenses. Heat resisting glass, such as Chance's ON20, can be usefully employed between the light-source and the film to reduce these effects.

The Achilles heel of the enlarger is the gap between the lamp housing and the bellows, which must be easily accessible to the film-holder. Scattered light from this region may easily fog the photographic paper. We learnt from our earlier discussion of emulsions that those with gently sloping characteristic curves are the fastest and least contrasty. The same is true of papers, and softer grades are more susceptible to fogging than the harder, contrasty ones. This does not mean that we have to take extreme precautions—a few odd pinholes of light will not upset our work in the slightest, providing they are not directed at the enlarging table.

Safelights that are not really safe are a more likely cause of paper fogging, and ones of unknown make should be regarded with suspicion until a test has proved their suitability for the work in hand. A piece of soft photographic paper can be placed beneath the safelight, and strips of it exposed for graded durations. Any safelight which produces darkening of the developed paper in less than about ten minutes should be sparingly used. Just because a piece of coloured glass transmits strongly in one region it does not follow that other colours are not getting through as well.

Preliminary Enlarging Work

Before we start the actual processing, we must supply ourselves with enlarging papers, dishes, solutions, tweezers and all the apparatus described earlier, and see that the solutions are ready for use. Now we can start:

(1) Select the best frame of film by inspecting with a magnifying glass. A watchmakers' eyeglass, worn like a monocle, is best, for

it leaves both hands free. Drying-marks usually occur on the back of the film and can be removed by gentle rubbing with a fine, soft, *clean* cloth; this should always be kept in a dust-proof container—a jamjar will do. Special anti-static cloths are sold for this work. Dust is brushed away from both sides of the film with a soft, fine-quality brush. This too should not be left carelessly about when not in use. My own is kept in a small plastic cylinder, and a cork, pierced to take the handle of the brush, not only fixes it to the cylinder but prevents the entry of dust. Almost any bottle or small container is adaptable for this job.

(2) When the film is absolutely clean it is placed in the holder, emulsion downwards: the emulsion is the dull side of the film. 'Sandwiching' completed, it is given a final dusting with the brush, and the holder, complete with film, is placed in the enlarger.

The opal lamp is switched on and, if all is well, some sort of ill-defined image will present itself upon a piece of white paper held in the masking frame on the table below. Focusing adjustments, by whatever means available, are carried out until the image is perfectly sharp. Special instruments, called 'focus finders', are sold to facilitate this. These, placed on the masking frame, deflect the light on to a frosted viewing screen, where a brighter and clearer picture is formed. With high degrees of enlargement the light is so diluted that any means of making focusing easier, as these instruments do, is to be welcomed. On the other hand, they are not necessities.

So-called split-image focusing, well known to astronomers years ago, is incorporated in some of the modern enlargers.

Test-strips

At the moment there is no need to dwell on the characteristics of enlarging papers. Let us lose no time and we can proceed to the methods of working out the correct exposure. For our type of work, there is nothing to beat the 'test strip', which shows us what we can expect to see on the finished positive enlargement. We are often reminded that test strip techniques died out years ago in all progressive darkrooms. Our advisers are, of course, the people trying to sell costly apparatus for doing the same work. At the risk of being termed archaic, my advice to the astronomical photographer is to forget such devices—nothing better than the test strip exists for our type of work.

Under the orange safelight, cut a narrow strip of bromide paper —preferably on a guillotine, although scissors will do. Place this in the masking frame and hold it down by the strips of material forming the mask. The opal lamp is out while this is being done. Next place a piece of black cardboard over all but a small area of the bromide enlarging paper. The opal lamp in the pre-focused enlarger is switched on and some of the negative's subject material —ideally a good cross-section of all the density ranges—will be projected on to the exposed portion of the emulsion. After, say, five seconds, the cardboard can be slid along to reveal, as well as the original, another strip of emulsion. This is given an exposure of five seconds, and we move the cardboard yet again, and so on. By the time we reach the last segment of our test strip, we shall have a sequence of exposed areas, of which the earlier ones have received much longer exposures than the later ones. The time interval of five seconds between consecutive tests has been chosen arbitrarily. Larger pictures require a longer interval; for when the size of the picture is doubled, its area is quadrupled, and will therefore require four times the exposure.

The test strip is next submerged in the dish of developing solution. At 20° C. or 68° F. the strip will be fully developed in about two minutes, the dish being tipped gently back and forth to keep the solution moving. Development occurs in three distinct phases. First, there is the induction period of perhaps half a minute, when nothing seems to be happening at all. This is followed by a busy phase when all the subject matter begins to appear, to be followed by the rapid filling in of detail. Lastly, the action apparently slows down again, there being little evidence of further blackening.

Photographic papers are developed to finality; negative materials are not, since prolonged development will over-darken them.

Resist the urge to remove the test strip before the two minutes have elapsed, even if some areas are absolutely black. Premature removal ruins the value of the device. Give the test strip a quick rinse in water and plunge it into the hypo; allow a full minute for fixing, keeping the solution in movement, before switching on the light. And before doing so, make sure the remainder of the bromide paper is back in its wrapping or in a light-tight box or drawer. Nearly everyone forgets to do this once.

Under bright illumination we can see what has happened to our test-strip. It will present a series of steps ranging from the very light areas, representing under-exposure, to (probably) completely black areas showing gross over-exposure. The exposure that was given to any strip can easily be calculated by counting its number from the least exposed end, and multiplying by 5.

Thus, if we require the same exposure as that of the fourth strip, we must enlarge for 20 seconds; for the sixth strip, 30 seconds, etc.

When selecting the most suitable strip, we should avoid those with jet-black tones, especially if the adjacent white areas are depicted as grey. At the other end of the scale we must discriminate against 'burnt out' whites devoid of detail, and blacks which are no more than greys. True black should only occur where the night sky is depicted (corresponding to clear, transparent parts of the negative).

Lunar and planetary photography has its own problems. For example, suppose we have got an excellent negative of the crescent Moon. This will tend to be a little over-exposed in the limb regions and under-exposed at the terminator. Through no fault of the photographer, the Moon (being a three-dimensional body) always produces this effect; the same is true of the crescent Venus.

A test strip of the lunar negative can be made in the manner described and this will show portions of the sky, the bright lunar limb, and the intensity gradient towards the terminator. A careful examination of the various segments of the test strip should reveal one which includes a correctly enlarged portion of the limb area. In other words, this region will not be a featureless white area, but

188

will contain all the various tones which, together, give the illusion of lunar detail. The same segment of the test strip will yield a terminator which has invaded the lunar disc, suggesting a false age; terminator detail, already thin upon the negative, will have been blacked out by over-exposure.

Other segments must be examined until one is found in which the terminator is nicely depicted. The limb region, on this strip, will be white, featureless and under-exposed.

Thus one region of our photograph of the Moon must have considerably more exposure than another, if the over-all appearance of the enlargement is to look right. Printing and enlarging papers lack the tonal range required to cope with the much wider range of the negative. Ignorance of this fact can lead to much wasted effort.

'Dodging' and Enlarging

Fortunately things are not quite so bad as they first appear and, in the case of the Moon, we can offset this difficulty to some extent by using a 'dodger'—a simple contrivance made of black cardboard. There are no hard and fast rules concerning its construction, but since it is intended to shade off the terminator region of the enlargement, while allowing other portions to have longer exposures, and since the terminator may be either concave or convex, I shaped mine like a crescent Moon. The 'dodger' is manipulated between the projecting lens and the masking frame, and is kept moving so that its shadow will not show a sharp edge on the finished enlargement.

(3) Suppose that the hypothetical test strip indicates an exposure for the terminator region of 10 seconds. Then the denser limb region will need longer: about 30 seconds ought to be enough.

The orange safelight is the only source of illumination, and the prepared 'dodger' is placed handy for use. The enlarger has been accurately focused, and the lunar image carefully adjusted in relation to the masking frame, which now contains a sheet of bromide paper.

With one eye on the darkroom clock, the operator switches on the enlarging lamp. 'Dodging' can take place at any time during the exposure—a good way is to start it 5 seconds from the beginning of the exposure; this allows unencumbered switching operations at the beginning and end of each exposure.

Successful 'dodging' is an art in itself. After 5 seconds have passed, the 'dodger' is inserted into the cone of light, well above the masking frame, so that its shadow falls on the terminator region. The edge of the shadow should be a great circle passing from the lunar cusps. Owing to foreshortening the north and south polar regions appear relatively lighter (corresponding to denser parts of the negative) and need longer exposures in the enlarger; these, therefore, need not be shaded. The 'dodger' is kept in continuous motion, and its shadow, while never allowing the terminator to register upon the paper, advances back and forth shading that portion representing the intermediate regions. This ensures a gradual merging of the terminator with the remainder of the disc.

After 20 seconds, 'dodging' is stopped; the enlargement is then given another 5 seconds, which, together with the 5 at the beginning, make up the full time of half a minute.

(4) The opal lamp is extinguished and the bromide paper is removed from the frame and placed in the dish of developer; complete and rapid submergence is extremely important. To assist this, a few drops of wetting agent should be added to the developing solution.

At a working temperature of 20° C. (68° F.) and with some agitation, the enlargement will be fully developed in about two minutes. Under the safelight it is difficult to gauge densities and assess the required degree of development, so the clock is our only reliable guide.

(5) When development is considered complete, the enlarged positive can be transferred with tweezers to another dish where it is rinsed in running water to remove excess developer. Alternatively, a stop-bath can be used before fixing.

Fixing is carried out in another dish, containing acid-hypo

solution; a hardener can be added if the enlargements are to be dried by heat. Close inspection of the bromide paper during the first few seconds will sometimes show a 'brightening up' effect as unwanted silver bromide is removed from the picture.

Again, it is important that all parts of the paper should be fully and rapidly submerged. Many enlargements in one dish can prevent new arrivals from being properly fixed and unsightly stains will develop when ordinary (un-safe) lighting is restored. Bromide paper is too costly to be wasted by carelessness.

It has long been my practice to introduce the papers face-downward to both developing and fixing solutions. Tweezers are gently prodded on the backs with restless movements and after a few seconds the enlargements are reversed in the dish to see what is happening to them.

It is false economy to be sparing with developing and fixing solutions—too little may well cause 'bald patches' during development.

Ten or fifteen minutes should be more than adequate for fixing. Prolonged fixing will tend to bleach the high-lights while every additional minute allows the fixer to soak more deeply into the paper, making its removal more difficult. It must be remembered that all traces of the fixer must be washed away if the enlargement is to be permanent.

(6) Washing for a minimum of thirty minutes in running water will remove the fixer; if this is not possible, enlargements should be immersed in seven or eight changes of water, accompanied by vigorous but careful agitation.

Despite thorough washing, some hypo will inevitably be left in the finished enlargement and while such pictures may last for many years, there is always the risk of gradual fading. Since the hypo is the culprit, a hypo eliminator bath must be used, which allows the initial washing time to be reduced to about fifteen minutes: the enlargement is placed in the eliminator bath for five or six minutes, and then washed for about ten minutes in running water.

Contact Printing

So much for the enlarging process. We seldom need to make contact prints from our 35mm. films, though this may have to be done with larger-sized films and plates. As the name implies, prints are made by contact; in other words, the contact paper emulsion actually touches the plate or film emulsion. A light above is switched on, as described in Chapter 2, and the denser portions of the negative shield, while transparent areas transmit, the light. Thus the positive made upon development is exactly the same size as the negative.

Complete printing devices, embodying lamp, pressure plate, masking frames etc., for definite sizes of papers, can be bought.

An easy way of making a contact print is first to lay a soft, yielding mat of felt, or similar material, on a table-top directly below a ceiling lamp. In the glow of the orange safelight, select a piece of contact paper and place this with its emulsion upwards on the felt. Next place the carefully-cleaned negative emulsion downwards on the contact paper, holding it down with a clean and polished piece of plate glass of sufficient size to more than cover the contact paper.

Test strips can be made as before, simply by covering, or uncovering, portions of the negative-masked printing paper at fixed intervals. The black card used for test strips can be easily manipulated upon the upper surface of the plate glass—there is no need to interfere with papers and negatives below it. Indeed, if these are moved the resultant test strip will be rendered worthless.

Test strips and prints are made by switching on the lamp above the apparatus—a 40 or 60 watt bulb will be of the right order. Exposures must not be too long, for obvious reasons, and inordinately short exposures will be difficult to time. An odd second may make all the difference between a good and mediocre print if the whole printing time is brief.

The successive operations of developing, fixing and washing are identical with those of the enlarging process, though the developing solutions may vary in strength for certain papers.

Enlarging photographs of the Planets

The enlarging of planetary images photographed with small telescopes presents the worker with certain problems. In the first place, the images themselves are necessarily small—perhaps only a millimetre or two across. How then can they be enlarged to reasonable dimensions without emphasizing 'graininess' and without losing contrast?

The eye's reaction to contrast is peculiar. Take for example, two photographs of Jupiter. They are made from the same negative on the same grade of paper and identically processed; their only difference is one of size—one photograph is five times as large as the other. Viewed from about one foot, the smaller one will appear more contrasty. Although both pictures contain identical ranges of tone, the eye perceives more contrast if the transition from light to shade takes place over a relatively small angular distance. By placing our larger picture five feet away, its angular diameter will be reduced to that of the smaller one and its contrast apparently restored. The effect is rather similar to that experienced by visual observers at their telescopes: contrast is much reduced with high-power eyepieces.

The degree of enlargement for any photograph depends upon its use. If it is to be mounted in an album it will be viewed from a short distance, and an image of Jupiter about the size of a sixpence will be large enough. But this would be of little use if it were intended to hang the photograph on a wall. There the intended viewing distance has an important influence on the finished print. With this in mind, the worker should endeavour to supply prints and enlargements which will show all the detail recorded upon the negative at the intended viewing distance. If this is done, no useful function will be served by enlarging the images still more.

Increasing Contrast

If the contrast of planetary markings is considered insufficient in an enlargement on the hardest paper, a second negative can be made. To do this we first have to make a positive transparency on a soft and preferably blue-sensitive emulsion which can be processed in a safely lit room. A soft lantern plate is ideal; film-strip positive fine-grain safety-film also serves. The aim is to develop this to a γ value rather greater than 1. For film, a 1:1 dilution of Promicrol for 5 minutes at 20° C. (68° F.) usually produces the desired effect. The secret of success is to increase contrast by easy stages, and, by so doing, retain the delicate detail which would be lost if contrasty emulsions or energetic developers were used. The original negative can be given an initial two- or threefold enlargement, or a contact transparency can be made under the even illumination of the enlarger. Too much enlargement will produce graininess. The exposure must be full, so that all detail on the original registers on the characteristic curve of the positive. Whites corresponding to the dense parts of the negative should not be 'burnt out', but should be light grey. Thus any detail in the denser parts of the negative will be recorded. The new negative is made the same way. If enlarging has taken place in the earlier stages, the negative can be made by contact. Again, exposure must be full, so as to record all detail and to forestall forced development (which would be necessary if the emulsion were under-exposed) leading to increased graininess.

Contrast in the second negative should be greatly enhanced. There is, however, one snag to this method: the new negative has still to be printed on a paper that may lack sufficient tonal range.

As an example of the queer effect this produces, we can consider a photograph of the planet Venus taken in ultra-violet light and showing faint but distinct markings. The planet is depicted at or near dichotomy—approximately half-moon shaped. Following the 'fattening-up' procedure just described, the fainter portions adjacent to the planet's terminator have disappeared, leaving a crescent-shaped image which gives an altogether false idea of the planet's appearance.

A second method is to print two negatives from the original one via positive transparencies. One of these contains the enhanced detail of the highlights, being made on a long tonal-range soft plate

to a low value of γ, but the darker portions adjacent to the terminator will be missing. The other, contrasty negative, made as
before but rather more fully exposed, will show the true edge of the
terminator but the remainder of the planet will be 'burnt out'
(*i.e.*, on printing would reveal featureless whites).

When these two negatives are printed—they have to be exactly
registered so that the images coincide on the enlarging paper—a
normal exposure is given to the contrasty negative which, by
itself, will show only the shape of the planet in more or less un-
relieved white. The exposure of the second negative should fill in
the planetary detail. No hard and fast exposure factors exist, and
data must be obtained empirically.

Minimizing Graininess

Inevitably the time will come when, despite all our efforts,
negatives of the planets, while showing some detail, will also
exhibit graininess. What can we do about this?

How much we can do depends primarily on the number of good
sharp negatives there are available. For this reason, I sometimes
make a large number of exposures of a planet in quick succession.
Forty or fifty over a period of two or three minutes will show little
evidence of rotation—even with fast rotating bodies like Jupiter.
Careful examination of the processed film will reveal, depending
largely on atmospheric conditions, several passable shots. These
should be marked in some way: I use a sharp point to scribe marks
on the negative close to the chosen images.

If all the exposures have been taken with a reliable shutter at the
same speed, all the planetary images on the negative will have
similar densities. Having fixed the degree of enlargement, a test
strip can be taken of one of the selected planetary images. This
will tell us how long the correct enlarging exposure will be.

Now we come to the crux of the proceedings. What we are
about to do is based upon the premise that all the graininess, in all
our planetary images, is randomly distributed. This means that
no two images have identically-placed clumping of silver grains.

Since so many clumps are involved, the chances of this happening are negligible. If therefore, we could combine a large number of images to synthesize the planetary enlargement, we should expect to lose a good deal of graininess while still preserving planetary detail. This idea is not new and was used to good effect by Lyot and others many years ago. I am not conversant with the actual methods employed by these astronomers, but they must be very akin to my own.

As ever, the success or failure of the process rests with the worker. He must present the successive enlarged images to the enlarging paper in absolutely acccurate registration. To facilitate this, white plastic tape lines can be stretched across the table under the enlarger. The projected shadow of the edge of the film-holder —one edge of the film frame—is then kept parallel to these lines, ensuring identical orientation of the planetary images. (This is assuming the 35mm. film-holder to be grooved just wide enough for the film.)

The position of the planetary images on the enlarging paper is of the utmost importance, and masking frames (though convenient) are not essential. A small wooden picture frame, or even two odd pieces of wood, will suffice for this job. In the glow of the safe light a piece of bromide paper is placed below the enlarger. By some means this has to be fastened immovably to the table. The picture frame, or the pieces of wood, may be used for this task and a few thin nails driven through will hold the paper between them and the table. The latter must also be firm and immobile. The pieces of wood must be accurately perpendicular to one another; the remaining two sides of the bromide paper can be held down with drawing pins or sticky tape if there is any tendency for it to curl up. Next we need a piece of white card, or Bristol board—an ordinary white postcard will do; whatever is used, at least two of its sides must form a right-angle, so that it can register against the sides of the picture frame or the two pieces of wood. This is important because the card has to be removed and replaced many times as the enlargement proceeds.

Still in the subdued glow of the safelight, the card is placed in position hard against the corner we have prepared for it. If, by some simple means, we can prevent it from touching the bromide emulsion, so much the better. Now the opal enlarging lamp can be switched on; the enlarger has already been focused, and the planetary image is arranged to fall on the centre of the white card. There are two ways of accomplishing this; one is by moving the film-holder in the enlarger, while the other, involving some modification of the enlarging table, may be easier. Instead of using the table top, fix the enlarging paper to a large sheet of plywood which can be pushed about on top of the table; it should be heavy enough to ensure that an accidental knock will not move it.

Check the orientation of the images; the operator will soon become adept at judging parallelism between the projected shadow of the edge of the film-holder and the white plastic tape line on the table, or in the second case, the edge of the plywood. Plastic tape can be used here too if necessary.

Having done this, and with the card pressed hard against its wooden guides, the outline of the planet's image is drawn upon the card with a pencil. A full outline is not essential; indeed, it is better to leave a few gaps in it, since this allows the edge of the projected image to be seen; a full outline tends to contain the image despite slight inexactitudes. Any conspicuous markings can also be pencilled in.

Next, the exposure time for each negative must be found. As an example, suppose that there are ten planetary negatives to be integrated and that our test strip has shown one minute to be the correct exposure. Each negative must therefore be exposed to the bromide paper for six seconds only. Whatever the number of negatives used, the total enlarging time must be shared equally between them.

After the initial setting up, the sequence of operations is as follows:

(1) Check the position of the image on card, as already outlined; extinguish the enlarging lamp.

(2) Remove the white card from the bromide paper; expose by

197

switching on the enlarger for the requisite time; switch off again.

(3) Replace the card in exactly the same position as before; move the next projected planetary image into the place vacated by the first; check the parallelism of the white plastic line with the projected shadow of the edge of the frame; check the image's registration with the pencilled outline; extinguish enlarger.

(4) Carry on as from (2) until all the images have been exposed.

Developing, fixing and washing are carried out in the usual way.

This is the basic outline of the technique in which readers can develop their own variations. Within reasonable limits, large planetary images are easier to manipulate upon the card. In the case of Jupiter an image about the diameter of a penny would be right. If the images are too small the difficulty of accurate registration—where even microscopic displacements would have disastrous results—become prohibitive.

Having obtained a good enlargement with good contrast and reduced graininess, others can be made in the same way—or the first can be photographed, in which case contrast should not be over-emphasized. Most readers will have seen pictures of the planets in which the darker bands merge with the night sky while the whites are featureless: this is the result of too much contrast. For this reason, if slow fine grain emulsions are used for photographing the enlargement, they must be developed to a low value of γ in a soft-working developer. 'Universal' type developers diluted with large volumes of water are suitable.

Alternatively, fast emulsions with their gently sloping characteristic curves can be employed. The image, falling upon these, must be large to overcome graininess, and this means that the camera must be set up within a short distance of the enlargement. A supplementary lens will have to be used if the camera cannot focus to short enough distances. The picture to be copied must be evenly illuminated and the lights well-screened from the camera; set the lamps well to the side, so as to prevent light reflected from the glossy surface of the enlargement from entering the camera lens. Processing is carried out in the normal fine grain developer followed by the acid-fixer-hardener solution.

For faithful copying of continuous tone subjects, the γ value of the emulsion should not exceed 1. Values greater than unity will enhance contrast, while those less than one will give softer tones than in the original.

Drying and Glazing

Enlargements and prints can be dried by one of two methods:
(1) Cold drying. Without special drying apparatus, it is usual to lay the paper emulsions face downward upon some absorbent surface, or alternatively, they can be pegged out upon a line like a row of washing. In both cases drying occurs naturally, and is accompanied by curling and bending of the paper. The usual method of straightening the pictures is to stroke the backs of them with a straight edge, or to pull them firmly and gently across the edge of the work bench. Having been made more or less flat, they can be placed between the pages of a large book—be quite sure none of them are 'dog-eared' before stacking more heavy books upon the first.
(2) Hot drying is a better method. For this we need a print dryer as outlined earlier (Chapter 11). With unglazed prints and enlargements the papers are placed emulsions uppermost in contact with the canvas cover. If placed face downwards, there is danger of the prints taking on patches of inferior glaze from the metal surface of the dryer.

Glazing seems to give another dimension to a print or enlargement and often greatly improves the work. Special glossy papers, yielding good shiny surfaces without glazing, can be further improved by glazing them on shiny metal plates.

Again, there are two main methods:
(1) Cold glazing can be accomplished on plate glass or a ferrotype plate—in fact all sorts of materials suggest themselves for this work. Perspex or Lucite and even celluloid sheets have been used.

All the surplus washing water must be removed from the print before it is laid face down upon the glazing surface, which has been freshly cleaned and uniformly treated with glazing solution. Another way is to soak the print or enlargement in a dilution of one of the proprietary brands of glazing solution beforehand. A thin sheet of rubber or blotting paper is laid over the paper on the glazing plate and the 'squeegee' roller used to ensure complete contact. Any air pocket left between print and glazing plate will be revealed as a matt spot in the finished glaze.

Prints and enlargements should leave the glazing plate of their own accord when dry; now and again a recalcitrant print will have to be helped off, particularly in the case of glass plates.

(2) Hot glazing is carried out in the electric print dryer, and a stainless steel or chromium-plated metal sheet is used—the latter being very hard and scratch-resisting. The work should be soaked for a minute or two in glazing solution, as before, and then 'squeegeed' to the metal plate; blotting paper can be placed over it before 'sandwiching' with the canvas cover. With this form of drying, there is often audible indication of the progress, for the prints crackle and click away from the glazing sheet. Do not try to hasten the removal of the prints—they will peel away when they are ready; on the other hand, do not leave them unattended for long periods, as prolonged heating can damage them.

Matt papers, without the glossy surface, can be polished or varnished to produce a pseudo glaze. Concoctions for these purposes can be made up or bought according to needs. In most cases the glaze obtained will be inferior to the bona fide article but, nevertheless, will show a marked improvement over the untreated matt print.

Trimming

Trimming if done with a guillotine is a simple business. Whether or not a white border is left round the print is purely a personal matter. Sometimes it is useful to leave a broad piece of border to write relevant details on; on no account write on the back of the print, particularly if it is on single weight paper: pencils push up ridges on the front, while ink may show through.

Mounting

The trimmed print or enlargement can be mounted on a suitable board with a special adhesive; do not use just anything which happens to be handy. Whatever adhesive is used, it must be spread evenly on both print and board to avoid 'lumpiness'. Pressure should be applied by a press or by flat weights, and particular attention paid to the edges and corners. With 'Cow Gum' and similar mountants the residue is easily removed if it seeps out from the edges of the print.

Sheets of dry mounting tissue, looking something like thin cellophane, may be affixed to the back of prints before trimming. One method is to lay the print, face down, on a piece of clean white paper. The sheet of mounting tissue is laid upon this and may be stuck temporarily with a hot iron—an electric soldering iron or the pointed end of a domestic flat iron will do admirably. It is only necessary to draw centrally across the back of the print and tissue, two lines at right angles to each other and parallel to the sides of the print. This will melt the tissue locally, and stick it to the print. Together they can be trimmed and placed on the prepared mounting board. The iron can be used again to stick the tissue to the board. Since the tissue is stuck to the print only along the two lines parallel to the sides, the corners can be lifted to reveal the tissue. The iron is applied to the exposed corners of the latter and thus the mountant is stuck to both print and board.

They are then placed in an electrically-heated press, the print being protected by placing a clean metal sheet over it. About a quarter of a minute of pressure at the correct heat—in the 60° to 80° C. region—should be enough to cement the print to the board.

In the absence of an electrically-heated press, a domestic flat iron can be used. One snag is that the print sometimes refuses to lie flat: when the iron is removed, up comes the print. A useful dodge is to roll something cold—a length of brass rod, an inch or more in diameter, for example—across the print behind the flat iron. This reduces the temperature and 'gells' the mountant while still maintaining pressure on the print. Under the hot mounting press this trouble is less likely to happen, for the mountant, being composed of shellac, loses its more volatile constituents during the heating. These are absorbed by the board and the print, and without them, the shellac cannot soften once it has been 'cooked'.

Retouching

Pictorial and portrait photographers can apply themselves to the tasks of improving their work with knife and pencil and brush, but the astronomical worker is concerned solely with fact, and any additions to or subtractions from his negatives will ruin their scientific value.

Conclusion

The new-comer to astronomical photography may perhaps have been appalled at the quantity of equipment that seems to be required. However, this does not all have to be bought or made at one fell swoop; the gradual accumulation of my own equipment— starting with the making of the telescope mirror—has been spread over more than a dozen years.

The field open to the astronomical photographer is limitless; new objects appear (e.g., comets, novae), others are never the same for two days running (e.g. the Sun), others, again, like the planets, are presented to the observer under ever-changing aspects, while new techniques, procedures, and photographic material are all the time being developed.

The amateur's work may not always be of scientific value— though often it can be—but it will be an unfailing source of interest and stimulation, and will introduce him to the many wonders of astronomy where they are properly to be found—not in books, but in the sky.

APPENDIX A

Working Data for Negative and Positive Magnifying Lenses

Negative lenses

The position of a Barlow or negative lens in the telescope draw-tube demands particular attention, for a small displacement will make a large difference in the size and position of the final image. Let

F = the focal length of the objective

B = the 'negative' focal length of the Barlow lens

D = the distance of the Barlow lens inside the focal plane

E = the extension of the 'new' focal plane from the back of the lens (*i.e.*, the distance from the Barlow lens to the ground glass focusing screen)

M = the increase in focal length, which is proportional to image magnification: the ratio of the effective focal length to the focal length of the objective itself

Efl = the effective focal length of the optical combination

Then,

$$(1) \qquad Efl = \frac{F \times B}{B - D}$$

$$(2) \qquad M = \frac{Efl}{F}$$

$$(3) \qquad E = B(M - 1)$$

Distances may be measured in either inches or centimetres.

Example

We have a 48-inch focal length mirror and a Barlow of 3 inches focal length. We wish to increase the image size by a factor of 5. What are the positions of the Barlow and the image plane?

This gives us:
$$F = 48 \text{ inches}$$
$$B = 3 \text{ inches}$$
$$M = 5$$

From (2) $\quad Efl = M \times F = 5 \times 48 = 240 \text{ inches}$

From (1) $\quad \dfrac{F \times B}{Efl} = B - D$

Evaluating,

$$\dfrac{48 \times 3}{240} = 3 - D$$

$$D = 2 \cdot 4 \text{ inches}$$

From (3) $\quad E = 3(5 - 1) = 12 \text{ inches}$

Therefore, to achieve an effective focal length of 20 feet, the Barlow lens must be placed $2 \cdot 4$ inches inside the Newtonian focus, and the focusing screen must be 12 inches behind it.

Positive Lenses

Let

$P =$ the focal length of the positive enlarging lens or eyepiece.

For the moment we can disregard the objective which forms the image in the prime or Newtonian focal plane. This real image can be projected through a positive lens in the same way that a lantern slide image is projected on a screen.

For our purposes the only important relationship is this:

$$(4) \quad M = \dfrac{E - P}{P}$$

Example

If we increase our image size by a factor of 5 with an eyepiece of $\tfrac{1}{2}$-inch effective focus, where will the new image plane be?

$$M = 5$$
$$P = \cdot 5 \text{ inch}$$

Evaluating (4) we get:

$$5 \times \cdot 5 = E - \cdot 5$$
$$E = 3 \text{ inches}$$

APPENDIX A

The above is approximate since, in this case, E includes a portion of the projection lens itself; the distance varies with the lenses used. A practical way is to measure E from half-way along the barrel of the eyepiece.

Using Commercial Cameras

The focal length of the camera lens, generally engraved upon its mounting, determines the image size when it is set at infinity. The size of the lunar image is easily found by dividing the effective focal length of the camera, or, for that matter, the telescope, by 110.

The magnification of a telescope is the ratio of the focal length of the objective to that of the eyepiece. Thus it is not only the eyepiece which determines the magnification of a telescope.

When a telescope is adjusted for normal visual observation, the emergent beam is parallel, and can be admitted to a camera with its lens set for infinity. The original camera image will be enlarged by the magnification factor of the telescope.

Example

A miniature camera with a 2-inch focal length lens is used with a mirror of 50 inches focal length and 1-inch eyepiece. What will be the size of the lunar image on the emulsion?

Size of lunar image in camera without telescope $= 2/110$ inch.

Magnification of telescope $= 50/1 = 50$

Size of telescope-camera image $= \dfrac{50 \times 2}{110} = \cdot 9$ inch diameter

Finding the Magnification of a Telescope

Point the telescope at a light sky and place the eye about ten inches away from the eyepiece. It will then see a small circular disc of light in the eyepiece—a greatly diminished picture of the clear aperture of the telescope, known as the Ramsden disc. Since it is a real image it can be measured (a transparent rule and a magnifying glass will facilitate the operation). Its diameter, divided into the diameter of the clear aperture of the telescope, will give the magnification. Stops and diaphragms must not be allowed to limit the clear aperture.

Example

Clear aperture of telescope = 6 inches
Diameter of Ramsden disc = 0·1 inch
Magnification = 6/0·1 = 60

Since the magnification of a telescope is the ratio of the focal length of the objective to that of the eyepiece, it follows that (the focal length of the mirror being 48 inches) the focal length of the eyepiece is

$$48/60 = 4/5 \text{ inch.}$$

APPENDIX B

Emulsion Speeds

Methods of measuring emulsion speeds vary from one manufacturer to another, and from country to country. Speed indexes
are either logarithmic or arithmetical. The British Standards
Institution and the American Standards Association have agreed
upon the same system, and use both methods. European Scheiner
and DIN are logarithmic.

On the logarithmic scale, every 3 degrees implies a two-fold
change in emulsion speed.

Example

An emulsion rated at 28° B.S.I. is twice as fast as one rated at
25°, but only half as fast as a 31° emulsion.

On the arithmetical scale a doubling of the numerical value of
the index indicates a doubling of emulsion speed.

Example

A film rated at 50 B.S.I. is twice as fast as one of 25 B.S.I., and
half as fast as one of 100 B.S.I.

Many factors affect film speed: the spectral sensitivity of the
emulsion, the spectral distribution of the light source, time-
temperature, and type of developer used, and the age of the film—
outdated film is slower—are just some of them.

For astronomical work, where speed is of vital importance, it is
false economy to purchase cheap outdated film. This advice is
based on bitter experience.

The following table gives approximate conversions from one system to another.

B.S.I. A.S.A. (Log.)	B.S.I. A.S.A. (Arith)	European Scheiner (Log.)	DIN (Log.)
37	400	38	28/10
34	200	35	25/10
31	100	32	22/10
28	50	29	19/10
25	25	26	16/10
22	12	23	13/10
19	6	20	10/10
16	3	17	7/10
13	1·5	14	4/10

Image Sizes and Exposure Data for the Moon and Planets

The linear size of the image of a celestial object is determined by the effective focal length of the optical system forming it. This linear size can be found as follows:

Consider the effective focal length (Efl) of the telescope—in inches or centimetres—to be a radius of a circle.

The circumference of this circle will be

$$2\pi \times Efl \text{ (inches or centimetres)}$$

The length of 1 degree of arc $= \dfrac{2\pi \times Efl}{360}$

The length of 1 second of arc $= \dfrac{2\pi \times Efl}{360 \times 60 \times 60}$

These expressions can be simplified by converting to radians. Since there are 2π radians in a circle the denominator is equal to one radian, or 57·3 degrees (206,265 seconds).

The length of one degree on the circumference becomes:

$$\frac{Efl}{57\cdot3} \text{ (inches or centimetres)}$$

The length of one second $= \dfrac{Efl}{206,265}$

We can now insert the angular diameters as determined from the B.A.A. *Handbook* or the *Nautical Almanac*.

Example

What is the linear diameter of the lunar image (31 minutes of arc) at the prime focus of a mirror of 48 inches focal length?

Linear diameter $= \dfrac{48 \times 31}{57\cdot3 \times 60} = 0\cdot433$ inch

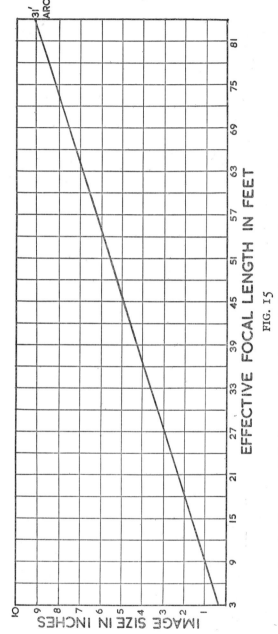

EFFECTIVE FOCAL LENGTH IN FEET

FIG. 15

Measure the diameter of the lunar or solar image in inches or centimetres (1 inch equals approximately 2.5 centimetres). Find the appropriate value on the vertical axis, and trace a line parallel to the horizontal axis to bisect the 31 minute of arc curve. Drop a vertical from this point and read off the effective focal length of the telescope on the horizontal axis. (One foot approximately equals 30 centimetres.) It must be remembered that both Moon and Sun change in angular diameter: slight corrections can be made for this.

FIG. 16

This can be made to yield information for lunar craters and the planets in exactly the same way as Diagram 15. The angular diameter of the chosen body must be known, as well as its measured image size.

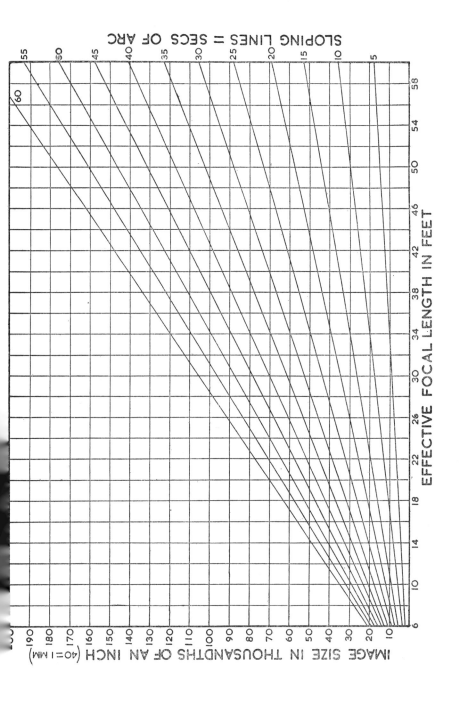

SLOPING LINES = SECS OF ARC

EFFECTIVE FOCAL LENGTH IN FEET

IMAGE SIZE IN THOUSANDTHS OF AN INCH (40=1 MM)

Example

Find the linear diameter of the image of Jupiter (45 seconds of arc) in the focal plane of a telescope whose effective focal length is 40 feet.

$$\text{Linear diameter} = \frac{40 \times 12 \times 45}{206,265} = 0 \cdot 105 \text{ inch}$$

Explanation of the Diagrams

Graphical representations of the above data are included for the reader's convenience. He must first find:

a.   The angular diameter of the celestial body.
b.   The linear image size of a known angular diameter in the focal plane of the telescope, to establish the scale.

Complete solar and lunar images can be measured without difficulty on a ground glass viewing screen. Owing to the faintness of enlarged planetary images some trouble may be encountered concerning their precise measurement. Here are some suggestions:

a. Insert a piece of fast film into the camera—it does not matter about graininess—and allow two close star images of known separation in Declination to trail across it. Dr. Steavenson has suggested using two stars of the Pleiades, Atlas and Pleione, whose separation is exactly 5 minutes of arc.

b. Another way is to allow the image of the planet to trail across the photographic emulsion. Upon development, the width of the trail can be measured with sufficient accuracy for our purpose.

c. An approximate way, using the focusing eyepiece in the back of a camera, is to estimate the number of times the image of the planet will go across the punched hole, of known diameter, in the film.

d. While the whole lunar image may be far too large, some idea of the image scale may be obtained by measuring selected lunar formations. When the Moon's angular diameter is 31 minutes of arc, the craters Copernicus and Tycho each subtend 48 seconds of arc. The diameter of Theophilus is 56 seconds of arc.

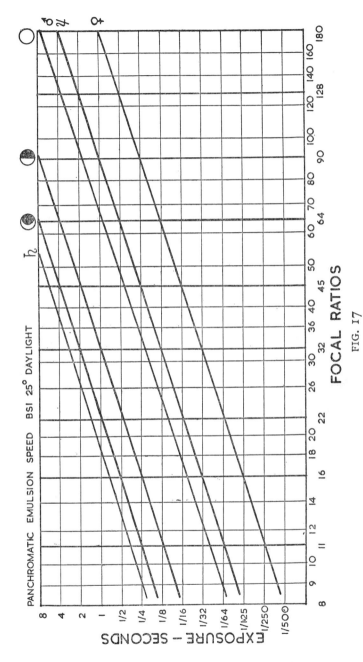

FIG. 17

This is fully explained in Appendix C

Having measured the linear size of the focal plane image, and knowing its angular diameter in degrees, minutes or seconds of arc, we can proceed as follows:

a. Find the image size on the left of the appropriate diagram.

b. Follow the line across to the right until it bisects the curve that represents the correct angular diameter.

c. Drop a vertical from this position to the horizontal, where the effective focal length of the telescope will be indicated in feet.

Example

Jupiter, with an angular diameter of 45 seconds of arc, yields a telescopic image one-tenth of an inch in diameter. What is the effective focal length of the telescope?

Following the 100/1,000 inch line across to the right until it meets the 45 second of arc curve, and reading the corresponding value on the horizontal axis, we find the effective focal length to be 38 feet.

Conversely, if we know the effective focal length and the angular diameter of the celestial body, we can discover the linear size of its image on the emulsion.

Should the image size be too large for the diagrams, we can reduce it by a suitable factor as long as we remember to multiply the effective focal length by the same factor.

The Effective Focal Ratio of the Telescope

Having found the effective focal length of the telescope, the next step is to derive the effective *f*/ratio. This is easily accomplished by dividing the *Efl* by the clear aperture of the instrument. Thus a 6-inch reflector with an *Efl* of forty feet will have a focal ratio of eighty (*f*/80).

Using the Exposure Diagram

This diagram is an attempt to provide a guide for intending

214

photographers of the Moon and planets. It is based upon many exposures, and it is hoped that workers will find it useful.

The vertical axis represents exposure time in seconds. The horizontal axis is graduated in focal ratios. Both scales are logarithmic. The top curve is that of Saturn, followed by those of the crescent Moon, the quarter Moon, the full Moon, Mars and Jupiter, and finally Venus.

The three superior planets are best observed around the times of their respective oppositions. Venus is best photographed when at maximum elongation from the Sun. The diagram is designed for these favourable occasions.

The exposures obtained from this diagram are those suitable with panchromatic emulsions, speed 25° B.S.I. (25 Arith. B.S.I.).

Now for some examples:

Example

What exposure must be given for Jupiter on a 25° B.S.I. panchromatic emulsion with our 6-inch telescope working at an effective focal length of forty feet (f/80)?

a. Find f/80 on the horizontal axis and project a vertical line from this position to the curve for Jupiter.

b. Project a second line from this point, parallel to the horizontal axis, to the vertical axis; here the exposure time will be found. In this case, one second.

A 28° B.S.I. emulsion will require only $\frac{1}{2}$ second; a 22° B.S.I. emulsion will need 2 seconds.

Example

What exposure must be given for the recording of Saturn upon a 25° B.S.I. panchromatic emulsion using a 6-inch f/80 telescope?

This is more difficult because a vertical line from f/80 on the horizontal axis reaches the top of the diagram before cutting the Saturn curve. In other words, Saturn requires more than 8 seconds' exposure, and we cannot attempt this without an accurate telescope drive.

There are two courses open to us:

a. To reduce the effective focal length, focal ratio and image size.

b. To employ an extremely fast emulsion.

At the time of writing, the fastest available emulsions are rated at 37° B.S.I., or 16 times as fast as the 25° B.S.I. emulsions.

Let us start from the point at which the Saturn curve crosses the 1 second exposure horizontal line. The point vertically below this on the 1/16 second horizontal line is close to the curve for the full Moon. A new curve for Saturn can therefore be drawn through this new point, parallel to the others. At $f/80$ it will be seen that the planet still requires more than 1 second's exposure on the fastest emulsion.

Whenever we double the emulsion speed we are, in effect, lowering the curves by one complete division on the exposure axis. In the above example we have doubled the emulsion speed four times and dropped Saturn's datum by four divisions, which is equivalent to a 16-fold increase in emulsion speed.

Exposures derived from the diagram may need to be doubled, or even tripled, if ultra-fine grain developers are used. Atmospheric haze, dirty lenses, tarnished mirrors and dewing-up likewise lengthen the necessary exposure.

It will be noticed that the curves stop a little short of the vertical axis. This is purposely done so as not to confuse focal plane exposures with those obtained through additional lenses. Exposures made in the focal plane, particularly that of an aluminized mirror, can be very much shorter than those predicted from the diagram.

Any glass filter will lengthen exposures by a definite factor which is best determined by experiment.

Differences of exposure time occasioned by changes in focal ratio can also be calculated: if the focal ratio is being increased, divide the larger $f/$ratio by the smaller, square the result, and multiply by the exposure time of the smaller $f/$ratio.

Example

If an exposure of 1/10 second is adequate for an $f/$ratio of 10,

APPENDIX C

what will be the correct exposure for the same object on the same emulsion at $f/100$?

Required exposure $= \dfrac{1}{10} \times \left(\dfrac{100}{10}\right)^2 = \dfrac{100}{10} = 10$ seconds

Conversely, when the focal ratio is to be reduced, so as to shorten exposure times, the new focal ratio becomes the numerator which has to be divided by the larger (original) focal ratio.

Example

If 8 seconds are required at $f/64$ to record a certain object, what will the correct exposure be at $f/32$?

Required exposure $= 8 \times \left(\dfrac{32}{64}\right)^2 = 8 \times \dfrac{1}{4} = 2$ seconds

APPENDIX D

Choice of Developers for Negatives

Two fine-grain negative developers which I can recommend from experience are 'Promicrol', a solvent developer made by Messrs. May and Baker Ltd., and 'Microphen' (containing a relatively new developing agent 'Phenidone') manufactured by Messrs. Ilford Ltd. Unlike most fine-grain developers, these actually impart more speed to the emulsion, allowing exposures to be reduced. The exposure diagram (Appendix C) is based on data derived from negatives processed with the above developers. Similar claims of increased emulsion speed are made for Johnson's 'Capitol'.

Ultra-fine-grain developers, on the other hand, yield soft negatives only at the cost of longer exposures; in my opinion this is too great a price to pay for virtually grainless negatives.

Manufacturers' instructions for both mixing and processing are supplied with developers; there is no need to deal with these topics here.

My usual practice is to use 'Promicrol' with an equal volume of water, and develop the film to ·7 gamma in accordance with the maker's tables. With Kodak Panatomic-X miniature film (25° B.S.I.) this is achieved in 18 minutes at 20° C. (68° F.).

Undiluted 'Microphen' has given excellent negatives on Ilford Pan F. (25° B.S.I.) in 10 minutes at 20° C.

Developers for Enlarging Papers

Among amateurs, the most popular and widely used developers belong to the prolific M-Q (Metol-Hydroquinone) family. Kodak D.163 and Ilford ID-20 are typical examples. Messrs. Ilford Ltd. also market a P-Q (Phenidone-Hydroquinone) Universal developer

218

which I can confidently recommend to those who suffer from metol poisoning.

The following developers are suitable for enlarging papers; there are many others not listed here.

Azol, Bromide and Universol	Johnsons of Hendon
Kodinol and D.163	Kodak
Cobrol and Contrast Developer 300	May and Baker
P-Q Universal and ID-20	Ilford

In addition to developers, these manufacturers supply full ranges of photographic chemicals, including fixers, etc.

The astronomical photographer who wishes to prepare his own solutions will find the necessary formulae in one of the following:

The Kodak Data Book of Applied Photography

The Ilford Manual of Photography

The British Journal Photographic Almanac (containing an extensive bibliography)

Enlarging, by C. I. Jacobson

These are but four works from a very long list.

APPENDIX E

Choice of Enlarging Papers

In astronomical work, normal to contrasty papers are required for 'straight' enlarging—*i.e.*, direct enlargements from negative to paper. When faint detail has to be 'fattened up', one method is to print the original—or modestly enlarge it—upon a soft paper and then to rephotograph this, thereby producing a more contrasty negative containing the original detail. Graininess is also reduced if the initial images are kept small.

I have used Ilford Multigrade Paper for this work. This is a material that is coated with a mixture of two bromide emulsions: one is a low contrast emulsion that is sensitive to blue light only; the other—a contrasty emulsion—is sensitive to yellow light, and contrast can be selected by printing the negative in light of the appropriate colour which can be changed at will by interposing one of five acetate filters between the enlarger and the emulsion. Blue filters are supplied for low contrast work, and more contrast can be obtained by using the yellow filters.

A very contrasty enlarging paper is Brovira Brilliant, made by Agfa. This is useful when 'thin' negatives are enlarged.

Care should be exercised concerning 'grades' of papers. There are no accepted standards, and a paper from one maker may be very different from that of the same grade coming from another manufacturer.

Developers, and particularly their dilution, play an important part in processing. The addition of more water, in most cases, increases the times of development and reduces contrast.

Photographic papers are made by the following:
Agfa
Fuji
Gevaert

Gulliman
Ilford
Kentmere
Kodak
Kosmos
Marchant
Mason

Miniature film (35mm.) can be bought from the following or obtained from the distributors.
Agfa
Ferrania
Fuji
Gevaert
Ilford
Kodak
Luminos

Keeping Photographic Records

From time to time within these pages I have emphasized the need for careful and methodical written records of all photographic work attempted. Each record should be jotted down immediately *after* the particular photographic experiment to which it refers, and this should be done before passing on to another experiment. This is essential, for one photographic exposure at a telescope is very like another, and few astronomical photographers are gifted with photographic memories. Also, while it is an excellent thing to plan in advance the photographic activities for any particular night, it is not necessarily wise to prepare a detailed sequence of operations to be performed at the telescope. Perhaps nine times out of ten the operator will complete successfully such scheduled photographic programmes, but, sooner or later, something—be it due to error, negligence or the weather—will occur that will compel him to make swift changes in his immediate plans. On the other hand this in no way implies that the operator should approach his telescope entertaining vague hopes that he will find something worth photographing. Of course he must plan a general line of attack, but this plan must be flexible enough to be altered at short notice, and only after each part of the plan has been successfully or unsuccessfully completed should the exact details be set down on paper. Records of photographic failures due to mistakes at the telescope are valuable in that they enable the astrophotographer to avoid making similar errors in future work: for the same reason it is wise to store the faulty negatives as well.

Perhaps a word of encouragement will not be out of place here. Do not be dismayed if the majority of the first astronomical pictures that you secure at your telescope are failures. All of the professional observatories produce considerable numbers of poor photographs: we see the excellent ones only.

Nevertheless photographic negatives are not necessarily ruined by under- or over-exposure at the telescope. Quite a high percentage fall victims to careless darkroom techniques, and that is why, in addition to notes of operations carried out at the telescope, we must set down details of the processing that emulsions have received in the darkroom. As far as the negatives are concerned this would seem to be sufficient, but obtaining good negatives is but half of the job: if we wish to display these pictures we must make enlarged prints of them, and such prints may involve special darkroom techniques if we are to explore fully the photographic possibilities of the negatives. Therefore it is wise to make notes concerning the printing and enlarging techniques—in fact notes of anything that seems to be important during the various phases of the work should be set down, for it is impossible for the astrophotographer to record too many details concerning his work. Usually, when the operator seeks information from his notebook, he is appalled by the incompleteness of his previous notes.

How then do we set about this all-important task? In the first place, we can say that it is possible to buy photographic books and diaries in which there are especially prepared pages for noting down photographic data. I have yet to see such books in which the pages are large enough to contain all the information essential for astrophotography, and it is as well to leave these for the more conventional forms of photography for which they are better suited. Nevertheless, the 'headed column' method of recording data is good, for each heading provides a stimulus to the mind of the observer, and it is likely that without headed columns some vital piece of information may escape his attention altogether and be irretrievably lost.

My own method is to use a spiral-bound school notebook; any ordinary notebook will serve, but the spiral-bound ones can be doubled back to form a single pad of paper that will not shut up in the dark of the observatory. I then select a whole page on which to record the data for one particular night's work—it may be necessary to use another page as well if there is a good deal of experimental work to be done. On no account cramp the notes: use plenty of space for them.

There is no particular order in which the various items should occur in the notebook, and I will at this point summarize the headings that I consider essential for the recording of astrophotographic data at the telescope.

1. *The Date.* This is an important item for, without a note of the date, the astronomical observation loses most of its usefulness.

2. *The time that the exposure was taken.* In astronomical work it should be the aim of the operator to time his observations accurately. In this respect the time is merely a refinement of the date, and the two items are complementary—this is evident if we imagine the unhappy state of affairs that exists when we have an accurate time record of an event that occurred on a date that was not recorded.

Usually Universal Time (U.T.), which is the same as Greenwich Mean Time (G.M.T.), noted to the nearest minute is sufficiently precise for most solar, lunar and planetary photography. If British Summer Time (B.S.T.) or Daylight Saving Time is used, the fact should be carefully noted, since this is one hour ahead of G.M.T. or the prevailing zone time. This hourly difference is easily remembered if we use '*Spring* forward. *Fall* back' as a reminder of the directions that clock hands have to be moved in the appropriate seasons. Ephemeris Time (E.T.), which is the most recent (1960) of all the various sorts of time, is used for accurate computations, and does not supersede Universal Time for observational work.

3. *Name of the astronomical object.* In the case of lunar close-up shots with supplementary lenses, only a small area of the moon will be recorded on the emulsion, and the identification of this area at a later date may be difficult, especially in the limb regions where libratory movements complicate the effects of foreshortening. The name and approximate position of the region should be noted down. If the name of the region is not known, then a small diagram of the whole moon should be drawn showing the position

224

of the region in relation to other well-known lunar objects. It is valuable to show also the position of the lunar terminator since this, to many people, conveys more information than the numerical value of the sun's selenographic colongitude that can be obtained from an ephemeris.

The planets provide whole images, so the problem of finding an area that has been photographed does not arise. All the same it is worthwhile to conduct a careful visual examination of a planetary disc, and to make a small diagram of what is seen. Sometimes planetary markings are faint and elusive and difficult to record photographically: a small diagram settles the problem at once. The name of the planet should be recorded beside the diagram.

In a similar manner sunspot positions can be recorded on quickly-drawn diagrams and it is useful to relate them to the preceding and following limbs of the sun. The latter can be found quite easily by projecting the sun's image on to a card from a stationary telescope: the image will move across the field and the preceding limb will be the first portion of the solar image to disappear. Likewise, the last portion to disappear will be the following limb. Correctly orientated cross-wires in an equatorially mounted telescope also give the orientation of the solar image.

Names of clusters and nebulae should be jotted down after attempts have been made to photograph them. Unidentified objects of this kind must have their positions related to nearby stars by means of a star map or pencilled diagrams.

4. *Seeing conditions.* The decisive role played by the earth's atmosphere in all forms of astronomical observation is so important that a reference to the prevailing seeing conditions should on no account be omitted from the astrophotographer's notebook.

Atmospheric transparency can be gauged by observing and noting any difference in the brightness of fainter stars in familiar constellations. Slight ground mist leading to longer exposures also deserves attention, and so does wind that buffets the telescope, but no attempt should be made to record photographically the restless, fuzzy images that are caused by violent atmospheric turbulence. Some sort of 'seeing scale' should be adopted by the astrophotographer:

there are many of these, but I find that for most purposes four grades are sufficient, namely:

Bad.—Work impossible: violent turbulence at zenith.

Fair.—Work possible with low magnifications: turbulence variable.

Good.—Clear skies: star images almost stationary at zenith.

Excellent.—Rarely-seen conditions: high powers reveal stationary star images and good diffraction rings.

5. *Photographic factors*

        a. Aperture of telescope.
        b. Effective focal length.
        c. Film: type and speed rating.
        d. Shutter speed.
        e. Filters.

The above items are so interdependent that none can claim precedence over its fellows. In most cases the diameter of the mirror or objective will be fixed, but the choice of the other items will be directly linked with the luminosity of the object that is to be photographed.

The effective focal length of the telescope may not be known and perhaps cannot be calculated until after the images have been measured, but the position of the Barlow lens or supplementary lens can be noted with respect to the draw-tube and the plane of the film. Rough diagrams with the essential dimensions are of value here, and do not forget the focal length of the Barlow lens.

The speed rating, the type and make of film, as well as the manufacturer's processing recommendations, are usually supplied on a slip of paper with the film. This can be stuck directly into the notebook with adhesive tape.

Shutter speeds are so basically important and obvious that it is unlikely that a record of them will be omitted from the notebook. The same applies to optical filters.

APPENDIX F

The Darkroom

So much for the more important items at the telescope. What of the darkroom? Perhaps it would be best to summarize briefly some of the items that can turn out to be important during the processing of the negatives and the printing and enlarging of the positives. These are:

a. Temperature of developers, fixers, etc.

b. Developing time: the time spent by the film in the developer.

c. Degree of agitation—continuous, intermittent, etc.

d. Concentation of the developing solution, and number of times used. Age of solution.

e. Wattage of enlarger or contact printer lamp.

f. Aperture of enlarger. This can be fixed but an iris diaphragm is used on many models.

g. Height of enlarger above enlarging table. Knowledge of this can save time and photographic paper, particularly when a long interval has ensued between two periods of darkroom activity.

h. Length of exposure under the enlarger or contact printer. This is governed by the type of photographic paper used and all the above items, with one exception: old developer should not be used in the printing and enlarging processes. By old developer I mean solutions that have been used, not those that have been made up for some time without use.

There may well be other items that the individual will think of recording in his notebook, but it is always easier to note a fact than to consider whether it will be a useful item or not later on. You will find that the short time spent in jotting down notes will be saved many times over, and there will be an all-round improvement in the photographic results.

APPENDIX G

Photometry

Astronomers spend much time photographing the heavens, but more often than not the beautiful pictures they produce are merely by-products of their work, for generally some deeper study is involved. Photometry is one such form of study, and its object is to compare light from distant celestial bodies with that of a local source in the laboratory. By such means astronomers deduce the energy, and sometimes the origins, of the distant sources of light.

In order to understand how this can be done, we may refer to Chapter 2 where it is pointed out that 'blackening'—that is, the formation of metallic silver—depends on the total quantity of light that falls on a photographic emulsion. There are many factors that influence this process: the frequency of the light is important, for blue light is more actinic than red, and a comparatively dim blue light can cause the same degree of blackening as a bright red light —at least, this is how it seems to the human eye. Again, if the reciprocity law is to be obeyed, the duration of the exposure given to the astronomical object should be the same as that of the local light source, and both types of image must be recorded on identical emulsion and submitted to identical processing.

Having attended to the above items, as well as others of minor importance that are not mentioned here, we should be able to compare the two types of images on a photometer or a densitometer. A densitometer has the advantage because it has a linear response to density, while a photometer has a linear *arithmetical* output which complicates the measurement of photographic density which progresses *logarithmically*. Nevertheless, we can use either of these instruments and, with their help, we can compare selected areas of·the astronomical image to areas of blackening caused by our local light source. This will enable us to evaluate the unknown in terms of the known local light source.

One method of imprinting the local light source is now described. The requirements are these:

a. A small tungsten lamp—a 6 or 12 v. car bulb will suffice.

b. A battery (6 or 12 v. to suit the bulb.)

c. A rheostat, or sliding resistance. The electrical resistance must be low—10 to 20 ohms—and the current rating high, say, 5 amperes.

d. A D.C. ammeter: full-scale deflection 5 amperes.

e. A neutral density step filter, or a neutral density wedge of glass.

The lamp is wired in series with the ammeter, rheostat and battery: a switch can be included if it is considered necessary, although it is almost as easy to disconnect one wire from the battery terminal. In operation the brightness of the lamp, and the ammeter readings, are controlled by sliding the variable contact on the rheostat. It will be noted that when the lamp is brightly lit there is more current flowing through the ammeter; so, by varying the resistance, we can choose light intensities corresponding to any of the current readings on the ammeter.

By setting up our lamp some distance away from a small piece of photographic emulsion—a metre should be sufficient distance— and by making sure that the light illuminates the film evenly, we should find, after suitable exposure and development, that the film has darkened evenly over its entire area. The same would not be true if the film had been set close to the light source.

Now, by repeating this experiment, but this time by using a stepped filter in contact with the emulsion, we should find, on development, a series of areas of different densities ranging from light (corresponding to the darker areas of the step-wedge) to dark (where the denser regions of the step-wedge had masked the emulsion). If the step-wedge is calibrated in densities we are now able to establish a definite relationship between the light source and the way it is attenuated by the various densities. For example, a neutral density filter of 0.3 density cuts the light intensity down by one half, and we can measure the decrease in blackening that takes place on an emulsion as a result of this.

Let us assume that lunar negatives have been made with exposures of one second at the telescope, and that we have carried out experiments that have enabled us to imprint an image of the step-wedge on to a piece of film at the end of the lunar series, again with an exposure of one second. After the film has been processed simultaneously and evenly, and afterwards dried, it can be placed on the densitometer, and certain lunar regions on it can be compared with the step-wedge image densities. For example, we may find two lunar regions with densities that match two areas of the step-wedge image. If we try the same experiment another night we may find that the lunar regions have 'moved together', or 'moved further apart' as far as densities are concerned, and this points either to changes in the amount of light reflected from these parts of the moon, or to changes in the spectral distribution of the reflected light. If we had taken colour filter photographs of the moon, and compared them with step-wedge images made with light of the same colour, we could have solved the problem.

Now the interesting thing here is this: as long as we can reproduce this local source of illumination whenever we need it, and this we can do by adjusting the brightness of the lamp to a definite reading on the ammeter, we do not necessarily need to know the exact value of the light source in candelas, or the light intensity at the distance of the film. Of course, in many cases this has to be done, but a large amount of work can be accomplished without knowledge of the absolute brightness of the local source. In a way this is like measuring the height of a post with a piece of string instead of a calibrated tape: we do not know the length of the string in inches, but we can measure lots of things with it, and make comparisons between the various lengths that we find.

Some readers will ask why the brightness of the lamp cannot be found from the knowledge of the amperage and the voltage which gives a measure of the wattage, or the electrical power. Well, if it were as simple as this there would be no problem: what we do not know is the luminous efficiency of the source; we do not know how much of the electrical power is wasted in heating the air around the glass bulb. Nevertheless, an approximate value of 11 lumens/watt is given for tungsten lamps. Precise values can be obtained for various wavelengths of light by comparing the lamp with a standard source, or by sending the bulb for calibration to the National Physical Laboratories.

The lunar example is but one isolated instance: photometry is a powerful ally to spectroscopy, for instead of using the integrated light of many wavelengths, significant changes can be measured in individual lines of the spectrum. Photographic photometry can accomplish things that are too difficult to do visually, for the eye is easily deluded.

As well as these things we can use the step-wedge images to determine the degree of development needed to bring images up to definite density levels, and we can plot our own characteristic curves for all conditions and types of emulsions.

It is not my intention to discuss here the construction of photometers or densitometers. Some of these instruments are very expensive indeed—well beyond the resources of most people—others are cheaper and less versatile, and there are others that can be made quite simply, such as the one described by S. Archer[1] recently, which costs less than £5.

---

[1] *A Simple Photoelectric Microphotometer:* S. Archer, *B.A.A.J.*, Vol. 70, No. 4, April 1960.

Astronomical Photography with Simple Apparatus

Several people have asked me to include within these pages material dealing with astronomical photography in its simplest form, so that the subject can be pursued with the minimum of apparatus and expense. In a way this is a deviation from the original purpose of the book, and if I attempt to satisfy these demands it must be made clear at the outset that something has to be sacrificed to simplicity, and we cannot expect to get results with modest equipment that are comparable to those obtained with complicated apparatus. Nevertheless, simple and easily constructed apparatus is within reach of most people, and, if skilfully handled, it is capable of producing interesting and worthwhile results.

The Pin-hole Camera

Now, as I pointed out at the beginning of Chapter 4, the simplest form of camera is the pin-hole camera, which consists of a light-tight box with a pin-hole in one side through which light rays enter to fall on a piece of photographic emulsion placed some distance away on the opposite side of the box. There are no lenses to focus, so, to obtain the sharpest images, the size of the pin-hole should be altered, or, better still, a selection of small apertures should be used. In a small camera of this type the images of the sun and moon are too small, for their sizes are proportional to the distance between the pin-hole and the photographic emulsion. If, therefore, we make the camera large, large enough to hold the observer, it will be all the easier for him to examine the images in the dark interior, and make the necessary alterations to the diameter of the pin-hole. But before we start ordering wood and nails and so on for the manufacture of very large boxes, let me hasten to explain that what we really need is an upstairs room with at least one window that can be blacked out with a blind or hardboard panel: the latter is better, since the blind may have pin-holes in it already. One of the many ways of fitting a selection of pinholes to the panel is to obtain a small circular tin lid: mark the centre of it, and scribe a circle from this point with a radius about half-an-inch less than the radius of the lid itself. Several apertures should be pierced through the metal at equally spaced intervals around this newly scribed circle, the diameters ranging from about 1/64 inch to 1/16 inch. A hole large enough for a fixing screw is drilled in the centre of the tin lid, then it is fixed to the hardboard panel though which is drilled a larger aperture that admits light to each pin-hole in turn as the lid is rotated on the panel. It is important that the pin-holes should be round and unobstructed.

In making our pin-hole camera in this way we have also supplied ourselves with a useful darkroom, and with two or three photographic dishes and a few chemicals we can experiment in astrophotography without a telescope or even a lens. For choice, the window of our darkroom should point either east or west, and possess an unobstructed view that will enable experiments to be made on the sun and moon when these bodies are suitably placed in the sky.

The sun throws a conveniently bright image which is most useful for allowing us to select the best pin-hole size, and when the sun is low in the sky, this image can fall directly on a small piece of contrasty bromide paper held against the opposite wall of the room. With a ten-foot 'throw' the sun's image will be about one inch in diameter: a piece of cardboard serves as a shutter, and the exposure time will be of the order of one second. Remember that the sun's image will be moving along the wall slowly, so that we must be sure to hold the bromide paper in the position that it will occupy when the exposure is made.

When correctly exposed, the developed image will show a difference in shading from the centre to the limb, and larger sunspots will be visible as light areas on the darker disc, since we have made a negative on paper. A partial solar eclipse can be recorded in the same way, if the window of the room happens to be pointing in the correct direction at the time of the event—if not, a small front-surfaced mirror fixed on a camera tripod could be used to direct the sun's rays on to the pin-hole from outside the window. In this case it is worth noting that, while the developed image is still a negative, the mirror has provided a reversal and the image is the right way round.

This sort of pin-hole camera will record the gibbous phases of the moon when the sky is reasonably dark. If the image cannot be detected, a sheet of white paper held within a foot or two of the pin-hole will serve as a projection screen for a smaller and brighter lunar image, and the distance can be increased gradually until its position is found on the wall.

We cannot use the very slow bromide paper that we used to record the sun's images, so we must choose very much faster materials if we are to record the feeble light of the moon; and these emulsions will need careful shielding before and after the exposures. Some type of box can be contrived quite easily for this purpose, and if the emulsion is fixed in the bottom, the lid can be removed prior to making the exposure with the cardboard 'flap-type' shutter. Afterwards, all processing must be done in total darkness.

For example, a 1/20-inch diameter pin-hole, throwing light of the full moon over a distance of ten feet, should produce an image that is sufficiently actinic to be recorded with an exposure of one second on Kodak 'Royal-X' Pan film and other extremely fast emulsions.

As far as results go, we do not expect fine detail to be recorded in pin-hole images of the moon, but this type of camera should be able to capture images of some of the larger formations, as well as the maria, and the bright ray systems.

So much for the pin-hole camera. It is severely limited, on account of its extreme simplicity, to the sun and the moon, as well as to any terrestrial scenery that happens to fall within range of its small 'eye'.

APPENDIX H

An Improved Camera

Greatly improved results will follow as a consequence of exchanging the pin-hole for some sort of lens or system of lenses, and if the experimenter has at his disposal opera glasses, field glasses, or, better still, a pair of prismatic binoculars, then the scope of his work is widened considerably; for any of these instruments may be used to project astronomical images on to the wall of his darkroom.

First, of course, he must enlarge the hole in the panel covering the window so that it will admit a circular beam of light that more than covers the clear aperture of the objective of the instrument that he has chosen to use. A card baffle fixed round the cell of the objective will ensure that no light reaches the far wall of the room save that which comes through the instrument itself. Once the sun's image has been found, focusing can be done by the usual method of turning the eyepiece mounting, or the knob between the two 'monoculars'. The resultant images should be sharp, and small sunspots should be clearly visible. Also it will be noted that the best definition coupled with the maximum freedom from achromatic aberration will be found in those images that are not quite centrally displayed in the field of illumination. This is because the earth's atmosphere introduces dispersion when celestial bodies are low in the sky, and this can sometimes be cancelled by using some of the non-achromatism of the lenses forming the images.

For photographic materials we have a certain freedom of choice. We can keep exposures long by slowing down the materials, or we can use faster materials with extremely short exposures with special shutters. There is ample room for experiment along these lines: for example, we can retain the longer exposures—though this is not really recommended—and use the naturally blue-sensitive bromide paper with a yellow filter placed in front of it: the filter will slow the material down according to the density and spectral response. Alternatively, contact papers could be tried, for these are much slower than bromide paper.

235

On the other hand, if the faster materials are preferred it will be essential to shorten exposure times, and the easiest way of doing this is to devise a focal-plane-type shutter consisting of a piece of blackened cardboard with a thin slot cut across the centre. Enough cardboard should be left on either side of the slot to more than cover the opening in the box protecting the bromide paper. An exposure is made by quickly moving the thin aperture across the front of the bromide paper so that the second area of blackened card replaces the first over the front of the box. After this, the aperture in the hardboard panel over the window can be closed to permit processing to be done in the glow of the red safelight.

Lunar images will be well detailed, and, as projected from prismatic binoculars across the room, too big, so the distance could be shortened to produce some improvement in the brightness of an image that has been reduced in size. When the diameter has been measured, the effective focal length can be deduced from Figure 15, and this can be divided by the aperture of the instrument to yield the effective focal ratio. Figure 17 shows the relationship between effective focal ratios and exposure durations for medium-speed emulsions, so there should be no difficulty in choosing suitable materials for lunar work.

This is all that I intend to say about cameras of this type: quite clearly there is considerable scope in this field for anyone with a natural flair for experimenting.

Small Commercial Cameras

All sorts of interesting astronomical experiments can be done with miniature cameras, or even old-type box cameras, but again I must emphasize that few of these cameras are ideal because their lenses are small, and will not admit enough light to the photographic emulsion. Nevertheless, these cameras have the advantage of being available to most households, and after they have dutifully rendered their annual crop of holiday snaps, it seems a pity not to make use of them for other purposes.

There are two distinct methods of using such cameras:

236

1. *The fixed camera.* A camera that is pointed fixedly at the northern or southern polar regions of the sky for several hours will produce evidence, in the form of star trails, of the diurnal rotation of the earth. With the larger aperture cameras, that record the fainter star trails, it is better not to make the exposures too long, otherwise there may be some confusion of the trails—two or three hours is enough. The problem of fixing a camera in this way should not prove too difficult, but there are snags which should be guarded against; one is the wind that rocks the camera mounting; another, the clouds that arrive during an exposure; a third, the 'dew' that blinds the lens of the camera when everything seems to be going well. These things, that are dear to the heart of the poet, are dear, in a different sense, to the astrophotographer!

Medium-speed emulsions perform well for this sort of work—faster ones are grainy and suffer from the effects of reciprocity failure. Furthermore, we can use the extra contrast that the slower emulsions give us, and if these negatives are printed on contrasty papers, we should obtain prints with good black skies and bright star trails.

Larger apertures are preferred for meteor and artificial satellite work; nevertheless, pictures of such objects can be obtained with the wider-aperture 35 mm. cameras. Box cameras may be suitable for recording trails of satellites that are both bright and slow moving—the American Echo 1 for example.

Faster emulsions are more suitable for this work despite their graininess, for the images are moving very much faster across the photographic field: slower emulsions may not record them at all.

2. *The Guided Camera.* The principles which govern the fixing of a small camera on an equatorially mounted telescope for long exposure work on the night sky were described briefly in Chapter 1. I extolled the advantages of excellent bearings and slow-motion drives, etc., yet I am still asked to describe how pictures of the stars can be taken with simple and inexpensive apparatus. So, assuming that some sort of camera is available, how do we set about the task of making a simple mounting for it?

First let us perform a few minor calculations to find out what we need if we make an arbitrary assumption that the star-images provided by our lens will be of the order of 1/1000 inch diameter. In order that their light will be concentrated on their respective points on the emulsion, our basic problem is to devise a simple mounting that will enable us to correct any displacements before they become serious. Let us assume also that the focal length of our camera is about 5 inches—this will allow us to include most of the more popular types of camera. Accepting the fact that perfect images are unobtainable with all apparatus, we now have to ask ourselves how much image-wandering we can tolerate, for we cannot hope to confine our 1/1000-inch star images to circular areas o photographic emulsion that are only 1/1000 inch across. So let us take, again quite arbitrarily, the figure of 1/500 inch as the diameter of the area of emulsion we need to contain our 1/1000-inch images, and we shall see where this leads us.

We perceive very easily that the small angle representing 1/500 inch at a focal length of 5 inches also represents—using similar triangles—1/50 inch at a 50-inch focal length, and an area 1/50 inch across, as observed through a one-inch positive eyepiece magnifying ten times, subtends the same angle as 1/5 inch does to the unaided eye at a normal distance of ten inches. This means that if we had a telescope of 50 inches focal length, and a one-inch eyepiece, we should be able to detect small changes in the position of the guide-star, and rectify these displacements before they became serious in the shorter focal length camera. This is, of course, the whole idea of guiding, and the problem confronting the experimenter is to provide himself with the guiding telescope.

A guiding telescope does not have to define star-images to theoretical limits, neither does it need to be achromatic, so almost any telescope can be used for this work if thickish cross-wires are placed in the focal plane of the eyepiece.

If no telescope can be found after much fruitless rummaging in likely places, then some improvised arrangement must be sought, and odd lenses, even old spectacle lenses of about one metre focal length (1 diopter) can be made into suitable objectives that can be mounted in cardboard tubes, etc. Small, short focal length lenses will perform quite well instead of more expensive eyepieces. Necessity is the mother of invention, and there are all sorts of simple and ingenious ways of equipping oneself with the essential apparatus. For example, we can return to the field glasses or prismatic binoculars, for these are able to project real and enlarged images over comparatively short distances; so the overall length of a guiding telescope made with these will be shorter than with conventional lenses. Eyepieces and cross-wires are needed, and will have to be set up some distance behind the instrument.

With independent focusing binoculars we can go even a stage further by removing one eyepiece, and by placing a small piece of photographic emulsion in its place: this will make a simple camera. The spare eyepiece can be set a few inches behind the second complete 'monocular' so as to enlarge the real image projected from it. For a ×8 binocular a distance of 6 inches is sufficient. Thus we have made a camera and telescope out of a pair of binoculars, but I must warn the reader that all instruments may not be capable of this transformation: in some cases the focal plane may not be accessible, other models may not be adaptable without sustaining damage in some form or other. In any case there are bound to be snags, but overcoming them is one of the pleasures of astrophotography.

Whether we own a small camera and telescope, or have converted a pair of binoculars, as described above, we still have to face the problem of mounting what we have. The equatorial is the only mounting that, with the movement of one axis only, compensates for the diurnal motion of the earth, thereby allowing the celestial bodies to be photographed for long periods. (For further remarks on this subject, turn back to Chapter 3.)

Our first requirement is some form of polar axis that can be moved easily by hand—all sorts of things have been used, ranging from bicycle steering columns to pieces of disused overhead shafting. Water pipes and associated screwed fittings have interesting possibilities, also; indeed, it is surprising that so many useless-looking pieces of 'junk' can be transformed into valuable astronomical equipment.

The English yoke-type is one of the steadiest forms of mounting, but in the present case we hardly need the yoke so much as a long, straight square-section of wood with metal spindles at each end. This beam will have to be supported on these spindles at an angle equal to the latitude of the observer, so that when he looks up one face of the wood he should find that it points in the direction of the star Polaris. One of the spindles should be near ground level: the upper one must be supported by such means as are possible—some form of heavy wooden tripod is not difficult to make: war surplus tripods may still be found in scrap-yards.

So much for the polar axis. We still have to arrange for the declination of both telescope and camera, otherwise we shall not be able to select the objects we wish to photograph; so what could be more simple than a sturdy plank of wood, say four feet long, five inches wide and one inch thick. A largish fixing hole drilled centrally through the broad face will allow it to be bolted directly to the wooden beam forming the polar axis, which, itself, is drilled at right-angles to the main axis, a little more than half-way up. A declination fitting that is too low is badly placed for the observer: one that is too high may hit the upper support of the polar axis. This wooden fitting must not be bolted up too tightly for it will have to be moved; on the other hand, it should not pivot too easily or it will move when the operator brushes lightly against it.

The plank becomes the platform for the camera and the telescope, or, in the absence of a telescope, it forms an optical bench for the spectacle lenses and associated mountings. It is recommended that the camera go on the upper end of the plank, and on the side adjacent to the polar axis: the observer needs the long straight side of the plank for the guide telescope. The optical axes of the two instruments should be approximately parallel to each other—a problem that does not arise with the converted binoculars.

The operator makes himself as comfortable as conditions will allow—this is most important, since an inch or two difference in the height of his eye and the eyepiece of the telescope can cause mild torture in a short time. His task is to direct the telescope and camera at the portion of the sky that he wishes to record. All sophisticated aids have been sacrificed to simplicity, and he has a defocused star image to guide on: a focused image might disappear behind the cross-wires, and any deviations of the image from the cross-wires must be corrected, as soon as possible, *by hand*.

Now I must admit that this sort of apparatus is by no means ideal for astronomical photography, but, with practice, the operator will find that his guiding will improve, and results will be more interesting. Even more important will be the knowledge that he acquires: this will be useful when he progresses to more complicated equipment later on.

GLOSSARY

Achromatism. An essential quality of a telescope objective, ensuring colour-free images. Achromatic lenses are constructed of two different types of glass, so that the dispersion of one cancels that of the other. Improved correction can be obtained with three lenses.

Aerial image. A real image (which is independent of eyepieces, focusing screens, etc.) formed in the focal plane of a telescope. Such an image can be observed by placing the eye approximately ten inches behind the focal plane and on the optical axis.

Airy disc. As a consequence of the undulatory motion of light all telescopic images are marred by diffraction (q.v.), and the objective is incapable of forming dimensionless star images in its focal plane. A star image consists of a measurable disc—the Airy disc—which is surrounded by, perhaps, several diffraction rings, according to the brightness of the image. The diameter of the Airy disc is inversely proportional to the aperture (q.v.) of the lens or mirror; the resolving power of an optical system is its ability to define such discs. The size of the Airy disc depends, secondarily, on the wavelength of the light.

Ångström unit. Unit of length for short wave lengths. 10,000 A.U. are equal to one-thousandth of a millimetre.

Aperture. (*a*) The clear aperture of a telescope is the unobstructed diameter of the mirror or object glass.
(*b*) The word aperture is often used by photographers for focal ratio (*f*/ratio), but this meaning of the term is not used in this book.

(c) The diameters of the Airy discs (q.v.), formed by two perfect but otherwise dissimilar telescopes of the same aperture are equal.

Astigmatism. Distortion of images caused by asymmetrically-curved lenses, *e.g.*, cylindrical lenses. These have more than one focal plane and cannot produce point images of point sources. Anastigmat lenses, corrected for astigmatism, are essential components of high-quality cameras and enlargers.

Candela. The international unit of light intensity, replacing the international candle. 1 candela equals 0·981 international c.p.

Colour index. A correction applied to the visual magnitude to yield the photographic magnitude of a celestial body.

Dichotomy. The Moon at the quarter, when the area of the illuminated surface is equal to that of the dark surface, is said to be at dichotomy. The term also applies to the two inferior planets, Mercury and Venus.

Diffraction. The wave motion of light is responsible for the spreading of rays at the edges of opaque obstacles; one result of diffraction is the structure of telescopic star images, the Airy disc (q.v.) and its associated rings being the diffraction pattern caused by a circular aperture and a point source.

Diffusion, Light scattering which occurs in translucent materials and by reflection from semi-smooth surfaces. Translucent materials include photographic emulsions and frosted glass diffusing screens of the sort used in some enlargers. White non-glossy paper is used to diffuse light by reflection for some photographic work.

Inertia. The quantity of photographic exposure required to cause threshold darkening in an emulsion, after which darkening occurs in a linear manner. Graphically it is the distance from the density axis to the toe of the emulsion's characteristic curve. Inertia represents a loss of emulsion speed.

Light Trap. Light traps, important items in cameras and developing tanks, etc., are wall-like protrusions fitting into suitable grooves in lids and other removable parts.

Lumen. The international unit of luminous flux. This is the quantity of light emitted, in unit solid angle, by a point source of one candela in one second. Luminous flux is the rate of emission, or 'flow', of light energy. Thus a source of light, measured in candelas, emits a luminous flux, measured in lumens per second, which, if allowed to reach a surface, will create an illumination intensity measured in lux or lumens per square metre.

Lux. The international unit of illumination, equivalent to one lumen per square metre. The foot-candle, equal to one lumen per square foot, is still used in a similar way.

Newton's rings or fringes. Patterns caused by constructive and destructive interference arising from reflections between plane or convex surfaces separated by thin air films. They can be observed by transmission if both surfaces belong to transparent media.

Null point. When two light areas of similar intensity are brought together for comparison, in a visual photometer, the brightness of one is varied, by some means, until it exactly matches the other. This is the 'null' point or position, and one area can then be measured in terms of the other.

Opal lamp. A light source mostly employed in photographic enlargers. Its construction is similar to a conventional tungsten filament lamp; the glass bulb, however, is treated in such a manner as to produce a large and uniform source of diffused light to assist the even illumination of the negative. Without condenser lenses these lamps tend to yield softer or less contrasty enlargements. Opal lamps of 100 to 150 watts are suitable for most amateur work.

Optical axis. A light ray, travelling along the optical axis of a telescope, passes perpendicularly and centrally through the planes of both object glass (or mirror) and eyepiece. A refracting telescope, in correct alignment, would be able to rotate symmetrically about its optical axis.

Presbyopia. Long-sight. A condition of the eye which makes it incapable of producing sharply focused images of near objects on the retina; a positive lens corrects, but cannot cure, this defect. Myopia, or short-sight, can be compensated with a negative lens.

Refraction. Light, travelling from one transparent medium to another, suffers a change in velocity; all such rays, other than those normal to the surface, are deviated. All lenses and prisms are dependent upon this principle. Atmospheric refraction results in the apparent displacement of celestial bodies (see also dispersion).

Seeing. Light from a celestial body, before reaching the telescope, passes through a considerable thickness of the Earth's atmosphere, and, depending on prevailing conditions, is subject to a greater or less degree to the refractive effects of turbulence in the various layers. Such turbulence may cause a general confusion and swelling of the star, or in other cases may give rise to jerky movements of the whole image. Often both effects operate simultaneously, each being the result of turbulent motions in a different layer of the atmosphere. Photographic work differs from visual in that the eye can perceive rapidly moving but clearly defined telescopic detail, whereas the astronomical camera requires tranquillity quite as much as sharp definition of the images. Photographic 'seeing' is judged to be good when a star image is observed to wander in a circle no larger than one second of arc in diameter; a three seconds of arc circle denotes average seeing.

Solvent. Generally, a chemical liquid in which other chemicals are able to dissolve. For example, a mixture of alcohol and ether will dissolve celluloid (mainly cellulose nitrate). Perspex, or lucite, dissolves in chloroform.

Total reflection. At a certain critical angle of incidence light rays, passing from an optically dense to a less dense transparent medium, cease to be refracted and, instead, are totally reflected. The right-angled totally reflecting prism which sometimes replaces the silvered diagonal in a Newtonian telescope reflects all incident light in this manner.

Virtual Image. An image, that can sometimes be mistaken for a real image, which is formed by rays of light that do not cross at a focal point though they may appear to do so. Such an image cannot be thrown on to a focusing screen for the light rays associated with it are generally parallel or diverging.

Index

247

INDEX

Miniature film, 221
Minimizing graininess, 195–9
Minor planets, 22, 148
Mirror, coatings, 50; covers, 65; deformed, 64; faulty, 52; parabolic, 48, perfection, 52, 54; performance, 62; reflex, 111; temperature, 24, 62; testing, 54, 55
Mixing vessels, 165, 178
Moon, 19, 52; angular diameter of, 18; apparent size, 20, 118; brightness of, 117; distance from earth, 114, 118, 119; earthlit, 142; eclipsed, 141; exposure factors for, 114–23, 214, 215; favourable apparitions, 118; image size of, 114, 119, 205, 209, 210; phases of, 114, 116–18
Moons, Galilean, 22
Motion, earth's diurnal, 17
Motion, proper, 148
Mounting, altazimuth, 56, 57; desirable properties, 56–8; English, 59; equatorial, 56; German, 59; 'gossamer'-type, 115; permanent, 61; press, 201, 202; prints, 201, 202; yoke-type, 59

Nebulae, 149
Negative, 30; developers, 218; eyepiece, 106; focal length, 104, 106, 108; ideal, 172; lens, 104, 106; lens formulae, 203, 204; post-development treatment, of, 173, 174; second, 194; thin, 45, 172
Neptune, 22, 147
Neutral filter, 159
Newtonian, telescope, 22, 48, 102, 122; focal plane, 70, 108
Newton's rings, 184, 244
Normal adjustment, 71
Null point, 124, 224

Objective, telescope, 46–51; microscope, 89
Objects, photographic, 18–24
Observatories, 61
Observer, comfort of, 48, 62
Off-axial rays, 105
Opacity, 37, 38
Opal lamp, 182, 187, 244
Opposition, 144, 215
Optical axis, 110, 245
Optical flat, 132, 133
Orion Nebula, 149
Orthochromatic filter, 159
Orthoscopic eyepiece, 144
Over-development, 171–2
Over-exposure, 171–3

Panchromatic emulsion, 43
Paper developers, 218, 219
Papers, photographic, 26, 44, 220
Parallax, reduction of, 134–6
Partial eclipse, 139
Perigee, 118
Permanent mounting, 61
Phases, lunar, 114–16; Venus, of, 23
Photographic, film, 25, 221; resolution, 120, 121; 'snags', 101
Photography, colour, 151; eclipse, 138–42; infra-red, 157, 158; large area, 18; lunar, 114–28; planetary, 48, 143–48; solar, 129–37; ultraviolet, 50, 102, 153–7
Photometers, 123–5, 136, 145
Plane mirror, 134
Planetary, enlargements, 193; exposures, 214–16; images, 143, 144, 209–14; photography, 21–4, 143–8
Planets, 21–4, 143–8; apparent diameters of, 21–4; minor, 22, 148
Plate, attachment, 75; compared with film, 83; cutting, 84; development, 168, 169; emulsions, 85; holders, 75, 76; photographic, 25, 26; storage, 84
Pleiades, 23, 149
Pluto, 22, 147
Point sources, 52
Polar axis, 57, 65
Polarizers, 133
Portable instruments, 56
Positive, eyepiece focusing, 88, 144; lens formulae, 204, 205; photographic, 31, 44, 182–202
Pre-focusing, 89
Presbyopia, 89, 245
Press, mounting, 201, 202
Pressure plate, 90
Print, dryer, 200; viewing distance, 193
Prism, compared with flat, 102; totally reflecting, 134
Prismatic eyepiece, 110, 111
Projected solar image, 134
Projector lens, 183
Prominences, solar, 139
Proper motion, 148

Ramsden disc, 205, 206
Range of papers, 189, 220
Rapid submergence of emulsion, 190, 191
Rays, axial, 105; converging, 71; diverging, 105; off-axial, 105
Reciprocity failure, 43, 69
Reduction, 174
Reflection, total, 246

250